Organic Chemistry

Laboratory Manual

Anne B. Padías

Department of Chemistry and Biochemistry
The University of Arizona
Tucson, AZ 85721

Third Edition

HAYDEN
McNEIL

ISBN 978-0-7380-3748-6

Hayden-McNeil Publishing
14903 Pilot Drive
Plymouth, Michigan 48170
www.hmpublishing.com

Padias 3748-6 F10

Table of Contents

Purpose of Organic Lab and This Manual

The purpose of this course is to teach how organic chemistry is "done." The objectives can be summarized as follows:

- To teach how to function effectively, efficiently and, most importantly, safely in a chemical laboratory.

- To teach how to make reliable and accurate observations, to interpret them and to report findings in a professional manner. Notice the primary objective of running an experiment is not to obtain product by following the "cookbook" directions found in the manual, but rather to try to interpret and understand what happened during the experiment.

- To teach how to use basic equipment and to perform common laboratory techniques.

- To show the experimental basis of theories and concepts that are presented in the lecture course.

- To teach how to THINK about organic chemistry and how to write down ideas in a professional manner.

This laboratory manual describes the specific experiments you will be performing in this course. Most experiments will be done by each student individually, but some experiments have been redesigned to allow for group work. I hope you will enjoy this experience and would very much appreciate any feedback.

The techniques necessary for each lab are described in a techniques manual, namely *Making the Connections: A How-To Guide for Organic Chemistry Lab Techniques* by Anne B. Padías. The required readings will be indicated for each lab.

Organic Chemistry Laboratory Rules and Regulations

Organic chemistry laboratories have a rather bad reputation as being dangerous. This reputation is still based on a vision of laboratories of about 50 years ago and on the omnipresent explosions whenever the hero in an action movie enters a laboratory. However, as you will find out, working in a laboratory is quite safe. All you need is a little knowledge and *a lot of common sense*.

We have recently become a lot more aware of the short-term and the long-term effects that chemicals might have on human health. The sweet smell of benzene and the odor of dichloromethane are now forever associated with cancer. Abbreviations such as DDT, PCBs, and dioxins now result in a reaction of fear from most people, and legitimately so. The word "chemical" conjures up a feeling of suspicion, even though everything around us is made up of chemicals in the true sense of the word. Chemistry has brought us society as we know it today, with nylon, antibiotics, painkillers, CD discs, computer chips, Walkmans, brightly colored fabrics, and low-fat margarine. As with everything, a balance has to be found.

In a laboratory environment, many dangers associated with chemistry, and in particular organic chemistry, are amplified. Explosions and fires can happen, but usually do not. For such eventualities safety rules are established and will be strictly enforced. Vigilance is always required. Any time a person is in a chemistry building, they should be somewhat paranoid and more attentive than in any other building.

An important part of any laboratory course is learning to perform experimental work in an appropriately safe and efficient manner. For this reason, your grade, as well as your own safety, will depend on your knowledge of the following rules and regulations. Most of them will already be familiar to you due to your experiences in other lab courses, but some will be new because of the unique safety hazards present in organic laboratories.

1. No one is allowed to work in the laboratory unless an instructor is present.

2. Unauthorized experiments are absolutely prohibited.

3. There is a very clear dividing line between the classroom area and the laboratory area in each lab. Classroom rules apply to the desk area, while laboratory rules strictly apply once the line into the lab section is crossed.

4. No smoking, eating, or drinking are allowed in the laboratory. Never taste **anything** in the lab.

5. Due to the danger of fumes and splashes, protective GOGGLES (or a full face shield) must be worn at all times by **all** persons in the lab whenever any experimental work is being done. This includes visitors, students, and instructors. Remember, your eyes are the most vulnerable part of your body.

6. Lots of people wear contact lenses. It has recently been shown that wearing contacts is not more dangerous than wearing glasses in the lab, as long as goggles are worn, but you have to be very aware of the fact that you have these contacts in your eyes. If you use contacts, remove them as soon as possible if an accident occurs.

7. Dress appropriately for lab. Due to the danger from chemical spills, a lab coat is required. Shoulders should be covered. Fully enclosed shoes are required. The clothing you wear should be close-fitting; billowy sleeves are more likely to catch on things, and thus a potential for breaks and spills.

8. Long hair must be tied back to keep it out of chemicals.

9. Gloves should be worn when handling toxic chemicals, in particular strong acid. Be aware that gloves are not "magic." The correct gloves have to be worn, depending on which chemicals are involved.

10. Know the location of the eyewash, shower, and fire extinguisher. Know how and when to use them.

11. Know the proper methods for disposal of all wastes:

    a. Solid waste goes into the crock located in the waste hood.

    b. Liquid organic wastes go in the appropriately labeled bucket in the waste hood. Do not overfill the organic waste bucket!

    c. Broken glass **MUST** be deposited **ONLY** in the appropriately marked boxes. Due to the danger of broken glass, the custodians will not collect paper trash containing glass.

    d. **Only** nonchemical, non-glass waste goes in the garbage cans.

    e. Only wash water solutions should go down the drain. Care must be taken to ensure that water solutions of heavy metals and water solutions having pH values greater than 9 and less than 6 do not go down the drain.

12. For most experiments digital thermometers are recommended. However, for certain experiments, mercury thermometers are irreplaceable. **Special rules apply to mercury thermometers because of the highly toxic nature of mercury. In case you break a thermometer, do not try to clean it up. You should notify the appropriate personnel immediately and they will take care of the problem.** Make absolutely sure you do not walk through the mercury-contaminated area. You sure don't want to track poisonous mercury back to your apartment or dorm room. To avoid breaking your thermometer, secure it at all times with a clamp.

13. Be considerate of your fellow workers. Clean up chemical spills immediately, including drips on reagent bottles. Most chemical burns originate from spills. Proper lab technique includes cleaning up spills **immediately**.

14. Never leave an experiment in progress unattended, especially if heating is involved. Should you need to leave the lab while an experiment is in progress, get your instructor or a neighbor to keep watch over your reaction while you are gone.

15. Nearly all organic compounds are flammable. The use of a Bunsen burner is therefore highly regulated. You must also remember that highly volatile compounds, like ether and acetone, can be set on fire by heating devices.

16. Aisles must be kept free of obstructions, such as backpacks.

17. Never fill a pipet by mouth suction.

18. Avoid contamination of reagents.

19. Use the cabinet hoods when so instructed.

20. Do not use any glass containers, such as beakers or crystallizing dishes, to get ice out of the ice machine. If it breaks, it is impossible to see the glass shards in the ice, and a fellow student could get seriously cut if they put their hand in. Use the plastic scoops attached to the ice machine.

21. Should any accident or injury occur to you or one of your neighbors, notify your instructor immediately so he/she can help minimize problems. If you get acid on your skin, start washing with water even before asking questions.

22. Immediately report any hazardous conditions to your instructor.

23. Immediately report defective equipment to the instructor so that it can be repaired.

Safety Agreement

1. I will obtain approved safety goggles and a lab coat, and will wear them at all times when any experimental work is being done by anyone in the lab.

2. I am familiar with the location and proper operation of the safety shower, the eyewash stations, and the fire extinguisher.

3. I will obey all instructions concerning the safe performance of experiments. I will use the hood when required, dispose of all chemicals and other materials as instructed, and promptly return all chemicals and reagents to their appropriate place when finished. I will not allow reagents or chemicals to become contaminated.

4. I will protect myself by wearing appropriate clothing in the lab. I realize that I must wear shoes in the lab and that open-top shoes or sandals are prohibited.

5. I will not attempt any unauthorized experiments, nor will I work in the lab without proper supervision.

    I understand that I will be ejected from the lab and may receive a failing grade for the experiment if I fail to abide by these rules.

    I also understand that the University does not provide liability insurance coverage for students and that I am responsible for making arrangements to cover the financial burden of injuries that may be incurred during this class.

Signature: _____

Date: _____

Print Name: _____

Course: _____   Section: _____

Instructor: _____

Laboratory Notebook and Reports

Consult *Making the Connections* for detailed instructions.

A Notebook is an essential tool in any laboratory experience. It has to be an accurate, permanent record of anything you did and observations of what happened during the lab period. It will become the record of your laboratory work, your process, your observations, and the outcome of your experiments. The experiments are only valuable if they can be reproduced, either by you or by somebody else.

A Lab Report is an official document relating your results and experiences in the lab in a more formalized manner than the notebook. The records you keep in your notebook will be incorporated in your report. The reasons for requiring reports are:

- To help you learn how professionals record and report their observations and conclusions based on their own laboratory experiences.
- To improve your scientific writing skills.
- To help you better understand your laboratory experience.
- To help your instructor evaluate your laboratory understanding and ability.

A Completed Lab Report will consist of the following parts:

- A title page with the experiment name, your name, course and section number, TA's name, date, etc., along with an *Abstract*. (typed)
- An *Introduction and Background* section (objectives), including a physical constants table and the chemical equation, if appropriate. (copies of the notebook pages)
- The *Experimental Procedure* (copies of the notebook pages) with a TA signature.

- Your laboratory *Observations* (copies of the notebook pages) with a TA signature.
- *Results and Calculations.* (copies of the notebook pages or typed)
- *Discussion and Conclusions.* (typed)
- *References*, if necessary.

The purpose for these different sections is described below in a timeline format; i.e., when and how should you write these parts of the lab report.

Before Lab

Before you come to lab, you should have finished the following **in your notebook**:

- Written the introduction and background section
- Written out the experimental procedure

During Lab

- Data and observations should be entered in the notebook
- Record spectra if appropriate.

After Lab

- *Results and Calculations*

  In this section you should list the *facts*. Calculate the determined values, such as the % yield or R_f values. Compare the data you obtained with the literature data, for example melting points or boiling points, retention times. List the important peaks in the spectra you obtained. Appearance of the product, e.g., yellow liquid, white needle-like crystals, purple flat crystals.

- *Discussion and Conclusions*

  This is where you demonstrate your understanding of what happened in the experiment. Consult *Making the Connections* for detailed instructions.

The whole purpose of the discussion section is to convince your instructor that you really understand what you did in the lab, and why, and where it can lead to, etc. THINK!

Although this is not an English course, spelling and grammar are important. You will be graded for completeness and clarity of your arguments. Poor grammar and/ or spelling can be a problem. You should write in clear and concise sentences. One good rule is to try to limit each sentence to one idea. Finally, make sure you *cite* your data and observations while *explaining* and *interpreting* your result.

- *Title Page and Abstract*
  It might seem odd that the title page is the last item in this list. The title page not only contains the experiment name, your name, course and section number, TA's name, date, etc., but also a typed *Abstract*.

  The Abstract is a brief summary of the important findings. Only values and facts crucial to understanding the outcome of the experiment should be included. A reader of an abstract should get a clear understanding of what the purpose of the experiment was and what the eventual outcome was. It should be clear and concise, and limited to 150–200 words.

How to Write a Formal Report for Organic Chemistry Lab

As a general rule, a formal report should be typed double-spaced and single-sided.

A formal report usually follows the format of an ACS publication; for example the *Journal of Organic Chemistry*. It has a title page, with the title of the experiment, the student's name, the

TA name, the date, and the course and section identification. The report itself should consist of the following parts: an abstract, an introduction, an experimental part, results and discussion, and references if appropriate.

Abstract: This should be very concise, less than 200 words, and state the objective, the results that were obtained, and how they were obtained. It should give the reader of the abstract enough vital information so that one would know the main points of what will be described, without reading the whole report.

Introduction: The introduction is a brief statement of the problem which will be tackled (for example, the synthesis of a particular compound) and how this problem will be approached.

There is a definite difference between an abstract and an introduction. The abstract summarizes the whole experiment, including the results, while the introduction should provide the background information and the general plan of attack *before* the experiment was started.

Experimental Part: The experimental part should describe all the practical information necessary to run the experiment and reactions described. I encourage you to take a look at an issue of the *Journal of Organic Chemistry* and look at the experimental descriptions to get a better idea of what is required. A trained chemist should be able to repeat the reactions based on the Experimental Section without having to consult any other sources of information.

A first part of the Experimental describes the available equipment in a section named "Instrumentation"; for example, which brand of Melt Temp is used or which IR instrument is used.

The main part of the Experimental describes the reaction or the technique in simple clear language. Each section starts with a title which is the name of the compound to be synthesized or analyzed by a certain technique, followed by the description of the procedure, including the amounts in moles and grams (and/or mL), reaction times and temperature, other specific reaction conditions, work-up procedure, purification, yield in grams and % yield, and identification. No calculation of yields are given; it is assumed you know how to do this correctly. The identification includes a melting point or boiling point and spectral data in text form, in this case infrared information. A typical experimental procedure is given below.

t-Butyldimethylsilyl vinyl ether (SiVE)
t-Butyldimethylsilyl vinyl ether was synthesized by modifying the synthesis of trimethylsilyl vinyl ether.[1] Dry tetrahydrofuran (THF, 50 mL, 0.61 mol) was placed in a flame-dried round-bottomed flask under dry nitrogen. n-Butyllithium (2.5 M in n-hexane, 32.4 mL, 0.08 mol) was added via a syringe. After 3 h stirring at room temperature under nitrogen, t-butyl dimethylsilyl chloride (11.16 g, 0.074 mol) was added dropwise at 0 °C over 20 min. After a further 2 h stirring at room temperature, the THF was evaporated. The residue was extracted with ether-water and the ether layer was dried with anhydrous magnesium sulfate. Upon evaporation of the ether and distillation of the crude product at atmospheric pressure, SiVE was obtained in 72% yield (6.8 g). bp 137 °C. ^{1}H-NMR (CDCl$_3$) : 6.45-6.36 (dd, J= 13.7, 5.8 Hz, 1H); 4.44-4.38 (dd, J= 13.7, 0.8 Hz, 1H); 4.10-4.07 (dd, J= 5.8, 0.7 Hz, 1H); 0.90 (s, 9H); 0.13 (s, 6H) ppm. ^{13}C-NMR (CDCl$_3$) : 146.44; 94.32; 25.63; 22.69; 14.08 ppm. IR (NaCl): 2956, 2930, 2885, 2858 (C-H stretck), 1630 (C=C), 1257 (C-O), 1018 cm^{-1}.

1. Lee, J.Y.; Hall, H.K. Jr., *J. Heterocyclic Chem.*, 1990, 27, 1653

Results and Discussion: The Results section should describe the results as such. Write about what you did and what happened, and the spectral data you collected. The Results should cover the **FACTS** only.

The Discussion section on the other hand is **INTERPRETATION**. The Discussion covers the topics usually covered in the Conclusion part of the informal reports. This is the part where thinking plays a more important role. You have to demonstrate that you understand what happened during the experiment. You discuss the results you obtained and draw whatever conclusions you can. How do you know you made what you think you made, and what other products could have formed? How would you know? Also discuss some or all of the following points: What did you expect to happen and what actually happened? Why? Can you explain the difference between the obtained results and the expectations? What did you learn about the reliability of the chemistry used, of the techniques and the equipment used? What did you learn about the chemistry? How could you improve the results?

It is sometimes difficult to separate the results from the discussion and it is your choice if you want to keep them separate or not. Each reaction has to be discussed both in the Results and in the Discussion, or discuss them one at a time in a "Results and Discussion" section.

References: If references are appropriate, include them. The references are referred to by using superscripts in the text. The ACS (American Chemical Society) format for references is used in the example above and is recommended.

1a

TLC Analysis of Analgesic Drugs

Analgesics are drugs that relieve pain while the patient retains full consciousness. The non-narcotic group of analgesics includes acetylsalicylic acid (aspirin) and acetaminophen. All these pain relievers also have anti-inflammatory properties, which make them useful in the treatment of the symptoms of arthritis. Recent research has led to better understanding of the mechanism of the pain-relieving action of these drugs. Acetaminophen, aspirin, and ibuprofen are all Non-Steroid Anti-Inflammatory Drugs (NSAIDs). This family of drugs inhibits the enzyme cyclooxygenase or COX. Acetaminophen and acetylsalicylic acid are known to acetylate Ser[530] of COX-1 and COX-2 isoforms inhibiting the synthesis of prostaglandins, which are potent mediators of inflammation. In contrast, ibuprofen is a competitive inhibitor and competes for the substrate binding sites of both COX-1 and COX-2. In 1971, John Vane was the first to show that aspirin exerts most of its effects by inhibiting prostaglandin synthesis.

Felix Hoffmann, a chemist at Bayer whose father suffered from rheumatism, has often been given the title of "discoverer of aspirin." According to legend, Hoffmann's father was taking salicylic acid, which was already mass-produced by the end of the 1870s, to treat his rheumatic condition. This drug, however, was terribly irritating to the stomach and had an unpleasant, sometimes nauseating, taste. Therefore,

Hoffmann took on the task of developing a less toxic replacement. However, acetylsalicylic acid may have already been produced by other chemists at the time. Therefore, it is difficult to determine whether Hoffmann truly developed a new chemical compound.

The relationship between the structure and activity of these drugs is also still under investigation. These drugs were not designed, but their structure is based on systematic drug modification of compounds discovered by chance. The chemical structure of these drugs is given in the table on page 5.

Chemical Identification

Identification of chemical compounds is one of the tasks a chemist is frequently called upon to perform. Compounds can be identified by comparison with known compounds. This is always true unless we are dealing with newly synthesized compounds in synthetic laboratories or with recently isolated natural products. Comparison of an unknown with a known compound can be accomplished by comparing the physical constants of the two, such as melting point, boiling point, density, etc., by comparing spectroscopic data, by comparing chromatographic behavior, or by measuring a mixed melting point. Spectroscopic identification includes the use of infrared photospectroscopy (IR), ultraviolet photospectroscopy (UV), nuclear magnetic resonance spectroscopy (NMR), or mass spectrometry (MS). IR and NMR are the most widely used methods for organic chemistry and will be discussed in later experiments. It should be understood that we do not necessarily need to have the known compound on hand, but can rely on literature data to identify our unknown compound.

A different approach to identify an unknown is by comparing its behavior in a chromatographic method with known compounds. In chromatography, a partitioning occurs between a mobile phase and a stationary phase, and the nature of these phases varies in different types of chromatography. In most chromatographic systems, the stationary phase is more polar than the mobile phase.[1] The stationary phase is almost always a solid. The mobile phase in gas chromatography (GC) is a gas, while in liquid chromatography (LC) the mobile phase is a liquid (solvent). Partitioning of the compound in question between the different phases occurs based on such factors as boiling point, and polarity of the stationary phase, of the mobile phase and of the compound to be analyzed. In liquid chromatography a column packed with the stationary phase, such as silica gel or alumina, is used.

A quicker and more convenient method involves a thin layer of the stationary phase deposited on a glass or plastic plate, therefore the name *thin-layer chromatography* or TLC. TLC has the advantage of being a much faster and simpler method than column chromatography. In TLC, compounds are identified by the position of a spot on the plate after development. The position of the spot compared to the solvent front corresponds to the R_f value of that compound in a certain solvent system and in many cases this R_f value can be used for identification.

Often a sample might be a mixture of several compounds. In this case TLC is a very powerful method, in which the different components of a mixture will reveal themselves as distinct spots on the TLC plate. These components can be compared to a mixture of known compounds for identification purposes.

For background information and technical and practical details about TLC, read the accompanying techniques manual Making the Connections.

Polarity in Organic Chemistry

Functional groups usually contain *hetero-atoms*, non-carbon atoms like oxygen, nitrogen, and sulfur. Since these atoms are all more electronegative than carbon, they attract electrons, making the bonds *polarized*. A molecule containing a heteroatom can be *polar*; that is, the molecule behaves similarly to a magnet that has opposite poles. Like a magnet has a north and a south pole, a polar molecule has an electron-rich and an electron-poor "pole." Also like a magnet, if two polar molecules are placed next to each other, the opposite "poles" will attract each other and stick together. The stronger the polarity, the stronger the attraction.

A brief introduction to a few of the common functional groups is shown below. Consult your organic chemistry textbook for a complete listing of functional groups.

The most polar of the functional groups shown in the table is the salt, which is an *ionic compound*. The least polar group is the methyl group which contains no heteroatoms, but just a simple carbon atom.

Type of Interaction	Structure	Name	Abbreviation	Polarity
Ionic forces	$-O^-Na^+$; $-C(=O)-O^-Na^+$; $-HN^-Li^+$	Salts	$-ONa$	Very strongly polar
Hydrogen bonding	$-C(=O)-OH$	Carboxylic acid	$-COOH$	Very polar
	$R-O-H$	Alcohol	$-OH$	
	$-\overset{..}{N}(H)(H)$	Amine	$-NH_2$	
Dipole-dipole interactions	$R-C(=O)-R$ $R-C(=O)-H$	Ketone aldehyde	$R-CO-R$ $R-CHO$	Polar
	$R-C(=O)-OR'$	Ester	$R-COOR'$	
	$R-C(=O)-NR'_2$	Amide	$R-CONR'_2$	
	$R-O-R'$	Ether	ROR'	
London forces	$-C(H)(H)-H$	Methyl	$-CH_3$	Non-polar
	$-R$	Alkyl substituent		

The idea of two molecules "sticking" to each other is really a rather simplistic view; instead, there are different ways that molecules interact with each other. These *intermolecular attractions*, which are much weaker than normal covalent bonds, take on several different forms: ion–ion forces, hydrogen bonding, dipole–dipole forces, and dispersion forces. For a detailed description, see *Making the Connections*.

In chromatographic methods such as TLC, the polarity will be of great importance in determining how compounds will behave during the separation. As the stationary phase is more polar, the more polar components of a mixture will "stick" more strongly to the stationary phase, and therefore move more slowly. The least polar components will move the fastest and therefore have the highest R_f values.

Required Reading
- Polarity

- Thin-layer chromatography

Aim of the Experiment
- Determine the composition of a series of over-the-counter painkillers using TLC.

Learning Objectives
- Understand the basic principles of polarity of organic compounds.

- Be able to deduce the relative polarity of organic compounds by comparing the functional groups.

- Understand the principles of TLC.

- Combine all information to make positive identification of compounds.

Experimental Strategy
Different over-the-counter analgesic drugs often contain the same active ingredient(s) and in some cases also contain caffeine. The structure of the common ingredients in these painkilling drugs are listed in the table on the following page.

In this experiment each student will be issued two glass-backed TLC plates coated with silica gel $SiO_2 \cdot xH_2O$. The silica gel contains a fluorescent indicator which will make it possible to observe the spots under ultraviolet (UV) light.

One plate will be used to run all the knowns or standards, and a mixture of these. All the standards and a mixture of all the standards will be supplied to you as a solution in 50/50 ethanol/methylene chloride. The R_f values of all the knowns will be determined.

The second plate will be used to analyze four different over-the-counter drugs (Motrin, Tylenol, Bayer aspirin, Anacin, Excedrin, or No-Doz), and the mixture of the standards will be run alongside to provide consistency between the two plates.

The spots will be observed by two different methods: by UV illumination and by exposure of the plate to iodine I_2 vapors. The spots can be marked on the plates using a pencil.[2] The different behavior of the different spots in UV and upon iodine exposure, along with the R_f values, will assist you to determine the active ingredients of the different analgesic drugs.

In addition to the five ingredients we are examining, the analgesics could contain some other ingredients, such as an antihistamine or a mild sedative. These will show up on the TLC plate as unidentifiable spots.

Procedure

Preheat a water bath on each bench to about 60 °C.

Collect two TLC plates and TLC spotting capillaries to spot the plates.[3] Lightly draw a line 1–2 cm from the bottom of the plate. Mark the first plate with the five points where the samples will be spotted, four knowns and the mixture of knowns. Mark the second plate with four marks for the unknowns and one for the mixture of knowns.

Prepare the developing jar by introducing enough solvent to cover the bottom of the jar to about 0.5 cm height. Introduce a filter paper folded to fit in the jar. Allow the solvent to soak the filter paper and let the atmosphere in the closed jar equilibrate. The eluent used is ethyl acetate containing 0.5 % acetic acid.[4]

Students will work in groups of four. Each student picks one tablet of the four available analgesic drugs. Crush the tablet using a mortar and pestle and transfer the powder to a labeled centrifuge tube. Add about 5 mL of a 50/50 mixture of ethanol and methylene chloride. Heat the mixture gently for a few minutes in the hot water bath.[5] Allow the solution to rest for about ten minutes so that the insoluble fraction can settle to the bottom of the test tube. Centrifuge if necessary.

Active Ingredient	Structure	Which Brand Names Contain These Ingredients?
Aspirin (Acetylsalicylic acid) (*ASA*)		Bayer aspirin Generic aspirin Bufferin Anacin, Excedrin
Acetaminophen (*Ace*)		Tylenol Datril, Excedrin Panadol
Ibuprofen (*Ibu*)		Advil Motrin Brufen Nuprin
Caffeine (*Caf*)		No-Doz Excedrin Anacin

Spot the first plate with the solutions of the standards provided by the preproom.[6] Place the TLC plate in the jar and allow the solvent to run up the plate to about 1 cm from the top. Indicate the position of the solvent front with a pencil as soon as you remove the plate from the jar.

Each student will spot the extracts of four different analgesics on the second plate, along with the known mixture. Develop the plate as you did for the first plate.

Visualize the spots under UV light and mark them with pencil. Place the plates in the iodine chamber and mark the spots.[7] Sketch the plates in your notebook with any necessary comments.

Calculate the R_f values for each spot and identify the ingredients of the different analgesic drugs.

The elution sequence is always dependent on the elution solvent. Very often the sequence is as follows: ibuprofen, acetylsalicylic acid, acetaminophen, and caffeine (most polar).

Notes

1. The stationary phase is always more polar than the mobile phase. The only exception is Reverse Phase Chromatography, in which the mobile phase is usually aqueous and more polar than a nonpolar stationary phase.

2. A pencil has to be used, because pen ink contains organic dyes, which of course would migrate on the TLC plate.

3. Never touch the surface of the TLC plate with your fingers, because the oils from your skin will transfer to the plate and be visible later. Always pick up the plate by the sides.

4. The acetic acid suppresses ionization of aspirin and ibuprofen, which eliminates the excessive tailing otherwise observed with these acidic substances.

5. The whole tablet will not dissolve as it contains insoluble binders, buffering agents, and coatings. Do not overheat; the ethanol/dichloromethane solution will discharge from the centrifuge tube if the boiling point of either solvent is exceeded.

6. Try to keep the spot as small as possible, but concentrated enough so you will be able to see the spots after developing.

7. The iodine chamber contains iodine and silica gel. The surface of the iodine is enhanced due to the presence of the silica gel, resulting in a high iodine vapor density.

Discussion

- Discuss the relative polarities of the components of the analgesic drugs based on their functional groups.

- Discuss the behavior of these compounds on the TLC plate (R_f value) in function of their structure and polarity.

- Discuss the choice of eluent.

- Summarize the results of your experiment: Which drug contains what?

Questions

1. Which compound will have the larger R_f value on a SiO_2 TLC plate using 10 % ethyl acetate/hexane as eluent: 3–decanone or 3–decanol, toluene or benzoic acid, cyclooctane or cyclooctanone? Why?

2. What does TLC stand for in today's experiment?

3. Arrange the following organic solvents in order of decreasing polarity and give their respective structures when doing so.
    Acetone – Heptane – Acetic Acid – Toluene – Methanol

4. Define R_f.

5. Arrange the following compounds in order of increasing R_f value on silica gel and explain your reasoning. Benzaldehyde, n–decane, benzoic acid. What effect would be observed if the TLC were run with a more polar solvent?

6. Calculate the molecular weights of all analgesics used in this lab.

7. How many moles of acetaminophen does a 500 mg tablet of Tylenol contain?

8. Why was a 50/50 mixture of dichloromethane and ethanol added to the crushed analgesic tablets?

9. Why is it advisable to mark a TLC plate with pencil and not a pen or marker?

10. Why is a small concentrated spot desirable in running a TLC?

11. Why was the mixture of knowns run on both TLC plates?

12. A folded piece of filter paper was introduced in the TLC developing chamber. Why?

13. Why must the developing solvent level at the bottom of the developing chamber be kept below the sample spot applied to the TLC plate?

14. Why do the sample spots increase in diameter as the TLC plate develops?

15. Why must the solvent front be marked immediately after removal from the developing chamber?

2a

Infrared Spectroscopy and Analgesic Drug Identification

Infrared (IR) spectroscopy is the quickest and easiest way to obtain information about the functional groups that may be present in a certain compound. It is commonly used for qualitative identification of organic compounds. It is one of the oldest spectroscopic techniques used in organic chemistry and it has retained its usefulness in the modern laboratory. In infrared we look at the absorptions (= peaks in the spectrum) of specific *functional groups*, and thereby obtain information about the structure of a particular compound.

Functional Groups and Infrared Spectroscopy

The properties of organic compounds, both physical and chemical, are governed by the functional groups. It is imperative that you become familiar with the names and structures of the functional groups as soon as possible. A complete table of the functional groups can be found in any Organic Chemistry textbook. Make sure that you can easily draw all the Lewis structures of all these functional groups.

As with other types of spectroscopies, the molecules will absorb the energy of the radiation. Infrared spectroscopy is, like other types of absorption processes, a quantized process, meaning the molecule only absorbs certain frequencies of infrared radiation. These absorptions correspond to energy changes related to the stretching and bending of chemical bonds in covalent molecules. IR spectroscopy is discussed in detail in *Making the Connections*.

Since the infrared absorptions are related to the stretching and bending of bonds in a molecule, the signals in an IR spectrum will give us direct information about the nature of the bonds in the compound under investigation. For example a molecule with the C=O double bond will have a different spectrum from a very similar molecule with a C–O single bond.

Specific functional groups result in easily recognizable absorption peaks in the IR spectrum. Most of the important peaks are in the 1600–4000 cm^{-1} region; a listing can be found in the IR chapter of *Making the Connections*. Comprehensive listings are available in the library, e.g., *Infrared Absorption Spectroscopy* by K. Nakanishi.

Beyond the main peaks, we can also use the multitude of peaks in the 1600–600 cm^{-1} region. This is known as the fingerprint region, and, even though we usually can not identify many of these peaks, a compound will have a certain pattern of peaks in this region, which is consistent from instrument to instrument. Be sure to double-check this "fingerprint" region to identify a specific compound. Reference spectra are available in *The Aldrich Library of FT-IR Spectra* in the library, or online.

The IR instruments are VERY expensive. Therefore you have to treat them with care and respect. All samples have to be prepared on your own lab bench, not next to the instrument.

Sample Preparation in IR Spectroscopy

Over the years, many methods have been used to prepare the sample in a suitable form to record an IR spectrum. The sample can be either liquid or solid. For liquid samples, the most common method has been to place a drop of the liquid between two salt plates; and for solids, KBr pellets are formed by grinding up the solid with solid KBr and pressing the mixture into a thin pellet using either a press or a sample holder with two screws.

We will be using IR cards, which contain a film of polyethylene $-(CH_2CH_2)_n-$ onto which the sample is deposited. For liquids, apply 1 drop of the sample to the middle portion of the exposed film. For solids, dissolve a spatula tip of sample in about 10 drops of dichloromethane. With a pipet, place three drops of your solution on the polyethylene film. The dichloromethane will evaporate very fast. Place the "dry" card in the infrared beam, and record the spectrum. In the event that a compound is not soluble in dichloromethane, another volatile solvent such as acetone can be used.

The polyethylene film can be cleaned by rinsing with ~10 drops of dichloromethane (or acetone). Make sure the solvent has evaporated before reusing the card.

Interpretation of IR Spectra

The IR spectrum has to be analyzed. A very effective approach to analyze the spectrum, and to make some sense out of the many peaks in such a spectrum, is outlined in *Making the Connections*. This outline gives you a step-by-step checklist of how to interpret the spectrum.

Aim of the Experiment

- Isolate the active ingredient from an OTC drug.

- Identify the active ingredient using IR spectroscopy.

- IR Identification problems.

Learning Objectives

- Understand how an organic-soluble compound can be isolated from non-organic soluble components.

- Perform a simple chromatographic separation.

- Calculate % recovery.

- Acquire the ability to identify functional groups in organic compounds.

- Be able to identify important peaks in an IR spectrum.

- Be able to match structures with IR spectra.

In the lab, you are to isolate the active ingredient from a common pain pill, which is given to you as an unknown, and identify the active ingredient by infrared spectroscopy. This experiment will demonstrate several techniques, namely extraction, filtration and spectroscopic identification.

Required Reading

- Extraction

- Solvents

- Melting point

- Infrared spectroscopy

- The chapter on IR in your organic textbook

Safety Considerations
Methanol is a flammable and poisonous liquid. Poisoning may occur from ingestion, inhalation, or percutaneous absorption. It will cause, in order of severity, headaches, fatigue, nausea, blindness, respiratory failure, and death. Death from ingestion of less than 30 mL has been reported. Methanol is a common adulterant of bootleg alcohol.

Active Ingredient	Structure	mp	Brand Names
Acetylsalicylic acid	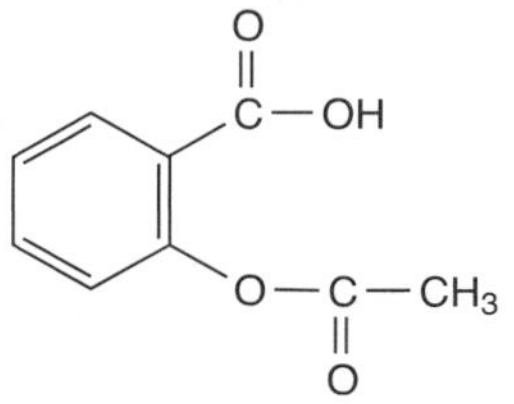	135–136 °C	Bayer aspirin Generic aspirin, Empirin
Acetaminophen	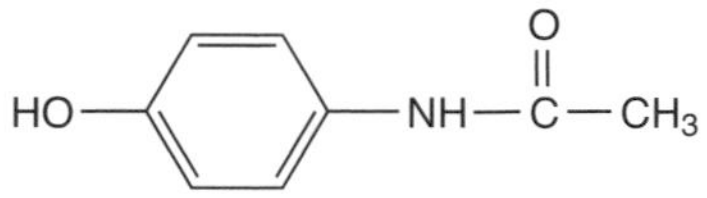	169–171 °C	Tylenol, Datril, Panadol
Ibuprofen	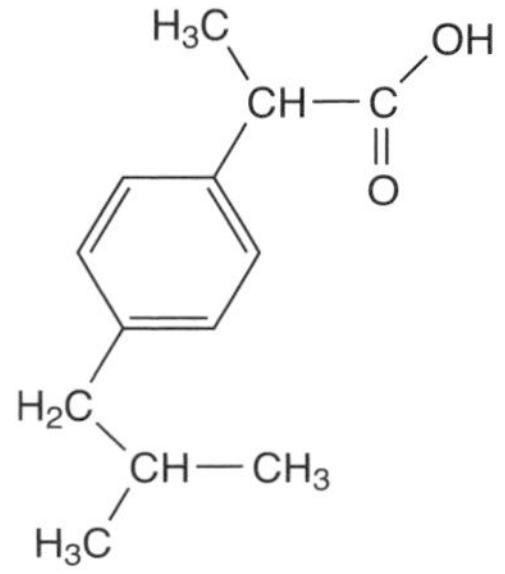	75–77 °C	Motrin, Brufen, Nuprin

Procedure

Preheat a water bath to about 70 °C.

Choose one of the unlabeled tablets. *Weigh the tablet before starting the experiment.* Crush the tablet to a fine powder using a clean mortar and pestle.[1] Place the powder in a centrifuge tube, add about 2 mL of methanol,[2] cap the vial and shake vigorously.[3] Allow the undissolved fraction of the powder to settle (a few minutes) and transfer the supernatant (= floating) liquid to a centrifuge tube using a Pasteur pipet. Repeat the process with an additional 2 mL of methanol and transfer the clear liquid to the centrifuge tube. Centrifuge the mixture for 2–3 minutes, if necessary, until the supernatant liquid is clear.[4]

Prepare a 2 cm alumina column using a 5″ Pasteur pipet[5] and add about 2 mL of methanol. Allow the methanol to drain, but don't let the column run dry. Add more methanol if necessary. When the level of the methanol has reached the surface of the packing material, transfer your solution of the drug component (supernatant) to the column using a Pasteur pipet and collect the eluting fraction in a small beaker. After the solution has drained again to the surface of the alumina, add an additional mL of methanol to wash the column and collect any remaining desorbed material.

Evaporate the solvent by placing the beaker in the warm water bath (or on a hot plate). To speed up the evaporation and to remove methanol vapors, connect a hose to the vacuum outlet on your bench and direct the vacuum over the solution. Alternatively, you can very gently blow air over the solution. When all solvent has evaporated, cool the beaker to room temperature.[6] It is essential to complete the evaporation of the methanol within 15 minutes if you are isolating aspirin, otherwise it may partially decompose.[7,8]

Collect the crystals on a Hirsch funnel and allow the crystals to dry for ~5 minutes by drawing air through the funnel. Transfer the crystals to a *tared* watch glass and break up remaining lumps. When the crystals are completely dry,[9] determine the recovered weight. Determine the melting point.[10,11] The melting point should give you an idea of which active ingredient you are dealing with.

Confirm the identity of the active ingredient by recording an IR spectrum and comparing it to the authentic spectra shown on the next pages. Use dichloromethane to dissolve your isolated compound, or switch to acetone if it is not soluble.[12] Also, run a TLC plate of your isolated active ingredient against a solution of the corresponding known compound. The eluent used is ethyl acetate containing 0.5% acetic acid.

Calculate the % recovery of the active ingredient of the drug from the pill based on the amount the manufacturer claims to be present.

acetaminophen	500 mg
acetylsalicylic acid (aspirin)	325 mg
ibuprofen	200 mg

Report

Your report should contain which active ingredient you isolated, the % recovery, calculated both from the weight you determined and the manufacturer's weight, the melting point of the isolated material, along with your interpretation of your IR spectrum. Notice that all spectra will necessarily contain the polyethylene spectrum (see page 14).

Notes

1. If the tablet is coated, remove the pieces of the plastic coating material with forceps.

2. Calibrate a Pasteur pipet by placing 2 mL of water in a volumetric cylinder and draw the water up in the pipet. Place a mark with a marking pen at the position of the meniscus.

3. Loosen the cap on the vial periodically during the mixing process to release any pressure built up in the vial.

4. Make sure you balance the centrifuge tube with a tube of equal weight on the opposite side. If the mixture is still cloudy, continue the centrifugation for another 2 minutes.

5. Insert a small ball of cotton in the 5″ Pasteur pipet and push it down to where the constriction begins. Add alumina to obtain a column of about 2 cm height and tap the pipet to pack the alumina. Clamp the pipet in a vertical position.

6. The volume of the liquid should be less than 0.5 mL when you stop the evaporation. The residue in the beaker will not necessarily be solid. Ibuprofen is rather low-melting and, moreover, the melting point will get depressed by impurities in all cases.

7. Prolonged exposure of carboxylic acid functionality in acetylsalicylic acid to methanol will result in esterification to the methyl ester and/or methanolysis of the acetate function, leading to the alcohol functionality and methyl acetate. The chemistry of these reactions will be discussed in second semester.

8. If no crystallization occurs, place the cool vial in an ice water bath to help crystallization, and scratch the glass surface with a metal spatula.

9. The ibuprofen crystals will remain somewhat sticky, even if completely dry.

10. Use a melt-temp capillary to determine the melting point. Some "sweating" or shrinking may be observed before the compound actually starts to melt. The beginning of the melting range occurs when the compound actually melts.

11. To put a sample in the melt-temp capillary, tap the open end of the capillary on the solid. Once you have some material in the tube, gently tap the closed end on the bench to make the product go down. If this doesn't work, drop the capillary through a long tube that is available in each lab. Don't worry, the little capillary won't break when you drop it; it will bounce up and down in the tube.

12. Acetone has a higher boiling point than dichloromethane, and isn't quite as volatile. Therefore you have to wait a little bit longer to make sure all the acetone has evaporated from your IR card before inserting it in the spectrophotometer; otherwise a carbonyl peak from acetone may interfere with your compound's spectrum.

Discussion

- Explain the logic of the isolation procedure used in this experiment (in chemistry terms).

- Present arguments defending your identification of the active ingredient based on the collected data.

- Explain the obtained IR spectrum in function of the proposed structure.

Figure 1: *IR spectrum of polyethylene film*

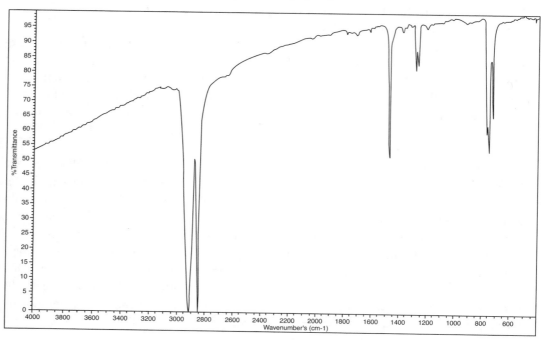

Figure 2: *IR spectrum of acetylsalicylic acid*

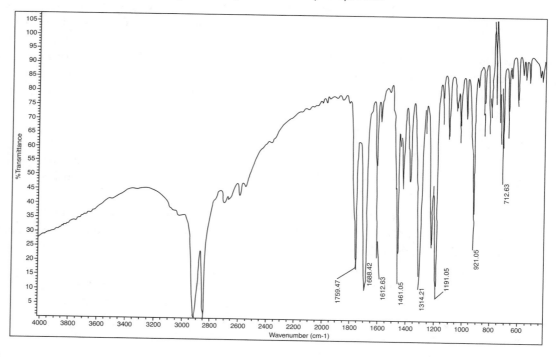

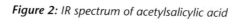

Figure 3: *IR spectrum of ibuprofen*

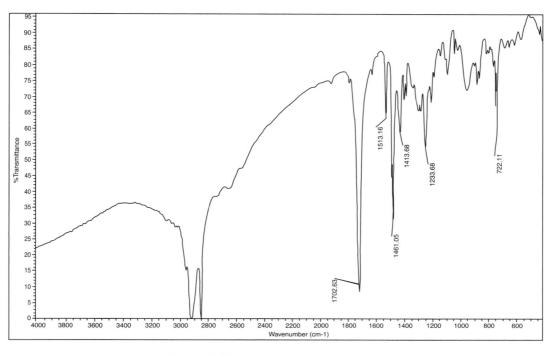

Figure 4: *IR spectrum of acetaminophen*

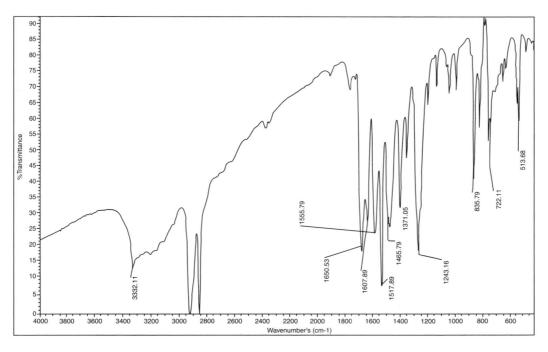

Questions

1. Name all the functional groups in the structures of the analgesics used in this lab.

2. Calculate the molecular weights of all analgesics used in this lab.

3. As a children's medicine, Tylenol has a major marketing advantage over aspirin: Liquid Tylenol preparations (essentially, Tylenol dissolved in flavored water) are stable, whereas comparable aspirin solutions are not. Aspirin has a phenyl ester functionality. When this ester bond is subjected to water for prolonged periods of time, it hydrolyzes to the carboxylic acid and a phenol derivative. Write the structures of all products.

4. Pure aspirin has a melting point of 135–136 °C. If aspirin crystals were not completely dried before the m.p. was determined, what effect could this have on the observed melting point?

5. Sketch the setup for a vacuum filtration of isolated crystals after extraction from an analgesic drug. Label all parts.

6. In performing extractions or washing, it is better to extract the sample many times with small volumes of solvent than only 1 or 2 times with a large volume. True or False? Why?

7. What role did the alumina column play in the isolation of the analgesic compounds? In other words, why did you use an alumina column in the lab procedure?

8. Why was the analgesic tablet crushed in the mortar and pestle?

9. Extra Strength Excedrin, a combination pain reliever, contains 0.250 g of aspirin and 0.250 g of acetaminophen. Propose in a flowchart format an extraction / recrystallization procedure that would isolate the analgesic components from the binding agents and buffers, and separate the analgesics from each other.

3a

Extraction
of Spinach

Photosynthesis in plants takes place due to a number of colored compounds (pigments) such as the chlorophylls (green) and the carotenoids (yellow, orange). Chloroplasts are the chlorophyll-bearing bodies of plant cells.

Chlorophylls are green pigments capable of absorbing visible light. The light is converted into chemical energy. The basic ring structure in chlorophyll is called porphyrin. Chlorophyll exists in two different forms, chlorophyll a and chlorophyll b. The only difference between the two forms is that one of the methyl groups in chlorophyll a is converted into an aldehyde function in chlorophyll b. Related structures to the chlorophylls are the pheophytins a and b, which do not have a central Mg^{+2} ion in the center but rather two protons.

Carotenoids are yellow and are also involved in the photosynthetic process. Carotene also exists in two forms, $\alpha-$ and $\beta-$, which in this case only differ in the position of the double bond in the terminal cyclohexene rings. Oxygen-containing derivatives of carotenes are called xanthophylls and are also present in the chloroplasts.

The different components of spinach have different polarities, and therefore can be separated by chromatography. Can you decide what the polarity sequence is of the different components? In this lab experiment we

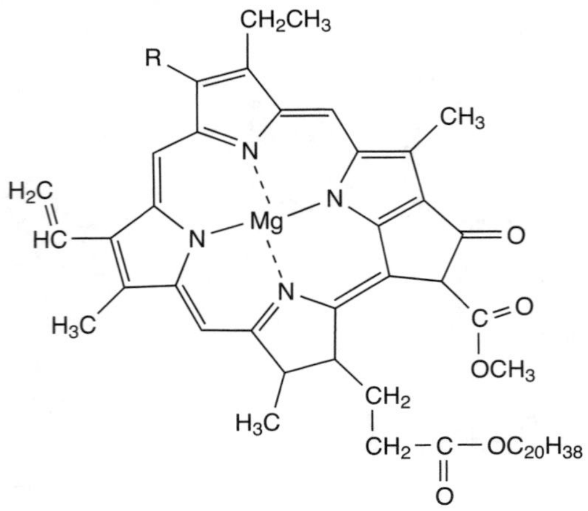

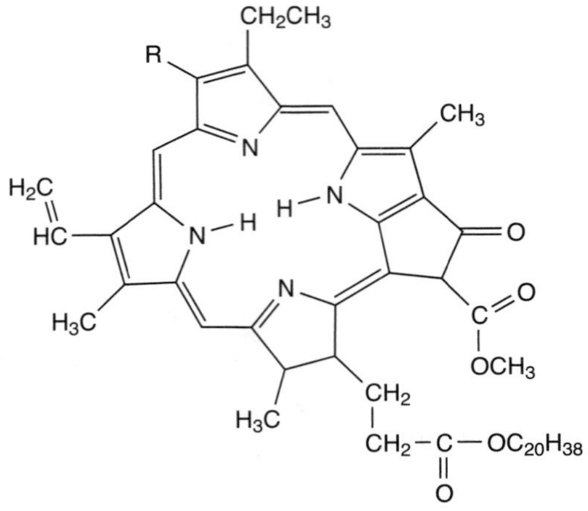

a R = —CH₃
b R = —CH=O

chlorophyll

pheophytin

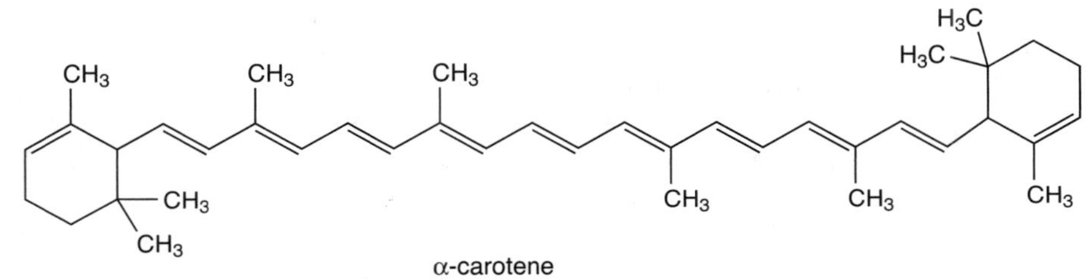

α-carotene

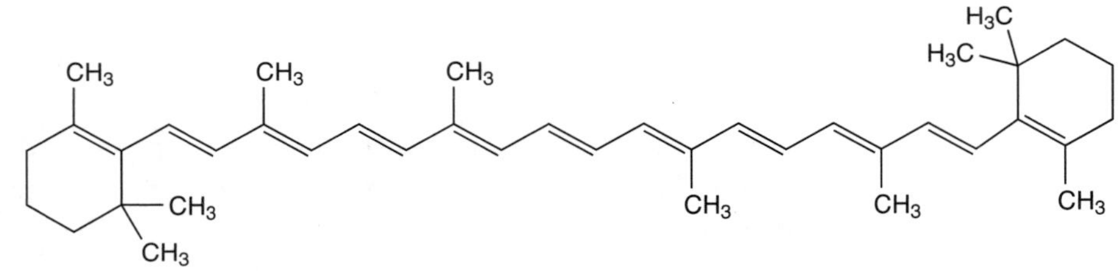

β-carotene

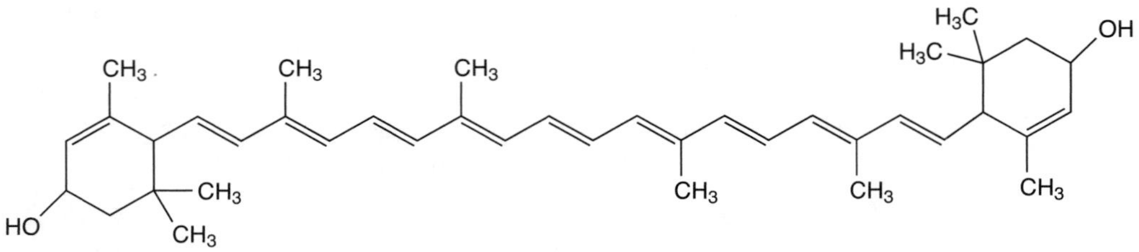

xanthophyll

will use column chromatography to separate the different components in different fractions, and then analyze the different fractions by TLC.

Aim of the Experiment

- Isolate different fractions of spinach components using column chromatography.

- Analyze the different fractions by TLC.

Learning Objectives

- Apply an extraction procedure to isolate active ingredients isolated from natural products.

- Observe the effect of increasingly polar eluent fractions.

- Learn how to analyze the different fractions collected.

- Correlate the structure of the components with polarity and behavior on a chromatographic column.

Required Reading

- Column chromatography

- Drying agents

Procedure

Prewarm a water bath to 70 °C.

The fresh spinach leaves can be prepared either for the whole class, or individually. This procedure is meant for the whole class. Fill the blender about 3/4 full with fresh spinach leaves, and add the following: ~10 mL of water, 2–3 tablespoons salt[1] and ~100 mL of a 75/25 hexanes[2]/acetone mixture. Run the blender until almost pureed, and add more liquids if necessary. Pour the mixture into a beaker. The organic layer should be **very dark green in color**. If it isn't, add acetone a little bit at a time[3] until the green color is mostly in the organic layer. Pour 3–4 mL of the mixture into each student's centrifuge tube. Add some hexane if necessary. Centrifuge for 1 minute, and transfer the organic (i.e., upper) layer to a test tube. Add anhydrous sodium sulfate to dry the solution.[4] Filter the dried solution using a 25 mL filter flask and vacuum suction. Allow air to blow over the solution by leaving the vacuum on until all (most) solvent has evaporated. Add a minimal amount of hexanes to redissolve, and transfer to a test tube marked as "E" (extract).

Dry pack a microscale column in a 5" Pasteur pipet with alumina (~2 cm).[5]

Use hexanes as the solvent to moisten the column.[6] **Do not let the column run dry**. When the solvent has drained to the top of the packing, place about 0.5 mL of the concentrated green solution on the column. When the pigment has all been adsorbed on the column, keep using hexanes as the eluent. Continue collecting the solvent eluting from the column (tube #1) until the orange band (carotene) is close to the bottom of the column. The orange band will be clearly visible. Collect the orange band in test tube #2.

After the orange band has eluted from the column, a more polar solvent mixture is added to the column, namely 75/25 hexanes/acetone solution. Use ~4 mL of the mixture, and collect the eluent in test tube #3. This polar solvent will move the green chlorophyll band down the column.

Once the green band has eluted from the column, switch to test tube #4. Six (6) mL of acetone should be sufficient to elute all organic material off the column. The column can then be allowed to go dry.

You should feel free to collect more fractions, as many as you feel are necessary. Be aware that not all fractions will be colored.

After the column chromatography, evaporate the solutions in the test tubes to almost dry.[7, 8] Remove the test tubes from the heat source as soon as only a few drops solvent remain. Add 2–3 drops of hexanes to the residues.

To run TLC (thin-layer chromatography) analysis of the different fractions, prepare a development chamber using the 75/25 hexanes/acetone mixture. Spot the four different solutions on the TLC plate using a capillary about 1.5–2 cm from the bottom of the plate.[9] Try to keep the spots as concentrated as possible. Run the TLC plate. Remove the plate from the chamber when the solvent front is about 1–2 cm from the top of the plate and mark the solvent front.

The spots on the TLC plate will be naturally colored. In the extract E you should be able to see all the different pigments listed here in order of decreasing R_f values:

Carotenes	yellow orange
Pheophytin a	grey
Pheophytin b	grey (may not be visible)
Chlorophyll a	blue green
Chlorophyll b	green
Xanthophyll	yellow

The different pigments on the TLC plate can be viewed under UV light (both wavelengths[10]) or after exposure to iodine vapors.

Calculate the R_f values for the different pigments. Draw the TLC plate in your notebook.

Determine the components present in the different fractions you collected from the column chromatography.

Notes

1. Either brine (saturated aqueous NaCl solution) can be used, or two spatula tips of salt can be added to the aqueous solution. The presence of salt in the water will force the organic component to the organic layer due to reduced solubility.

2. Hexanes is a mixture of several hexane isomers. It is cheaper than pure n–hexane.

3. Add the acetone a drop at a time, and stir the beaker content with a spatula to see the result after each addition.

4. Anhydrous sodium sulfate will add water to its crystal structure. Add a spatula tip full of the solid sodium sulfate and swirl the solution. The solution will become more clear as water is removed. You will know you have added enough sodium sulfate, if it doesn't clump anymore.

5. Use the Dry Pack Method. Clamp a short Pasteur pipet in an upright position. Place a small ball of cotton in the bottom of the pipet and push it into position. Fill the Pasteur pipet with dry adsorbent to a height of about 3 cm, using a folded piece of paper as a funnel. Gently tap the column to make the adsorbent settle and eliminate any empty spaces. Add solvent using a pipet and allow the adsorbent to be moistened slowly. Only add the solvent when you are ready to start the chromatography, because the column can never be allowed to run dry once the solvent has been added.

6. Have all solvents ready before you start running the column. You will need approximately: 3–4 mL of hexanes, 8 mL of 75/25 hexanes/acetone, > 6 mL of acetone.

7. This is accomplished by placing the test tube in a warm water bath and passing an airstream over the solution.

8. Most of these highly conjugated compounds are heat- and oxygen-sensitive and will decompose upon extensive heating.

9. Spot these samples repeatedly on the TLC plate.

10. Long exposure, ~2 minutes, to the long UV wavelength will result in a strong absorption of the chlorophyll spots.

Discussion

• Discuss the extraction procedure used to obtain the concentrated extract. Why are things done the way they are?

• Discuss the polarity of the different components in function of their structure.

• Discuss the behavior of the different components on the column and TLC.

• Discuss the choice of eluents.

Questions

1. Why was it important to know the structures of the components of spinach before you came to class today?

2. Pheophytins are less polar than chlorophylls, as shown by their respective R_f values. Write out the Lewis structures for each and explain why.

3. In the extraction of spinach experiment, the first band coming off the column ended up as the highest spot on the TLC plate. Explain.

4. Which compound, benzaldehyde, *n*-decane, or benzoic acid, will be eluted first and which one will be eluted last in column chromatography? Explain.

5. Why is xanthophyll less mobile on a silica gel column, and why does it have a lower R_f value than the β–carotene?

6. Describe how you would make 200 mL of a 0.5 M solution of β–carotene in dichloromethane.

7. Identify the functional groups in chlorophyll. (The five-membered unsaturated N-containing rings are called pyrroles.)

8. Why was it necessary to wet the alumina column with a solvent before running a sample? Why was hexane used, and not acetone, dichloromethane, or methanol?

9. The carotenes and xanthophylls are similar in color (yellow to orange), yet their R_f values are at opposite ends of the range for spinach leaf pigments. Explain.

10. What is the reason for the use of a drying agent such as sodium sulfate after performing an extraction?

4a

Recrystallization

When organic substances are synthesized in the laboratory or isolated from plants, they will obviously contain impurities. Several techniques for purifying these compounds have been developed. The most basic technique for the purification of organic solids is recrystallization, which relies on the different solubilities of solutes in a solvent. Most organic compounds will be soluble in common organic solvents, such as acetone, hexane, or toluene. Compounds which are less soluble will crystallize first upon cooling. *The crystallization process itself helps in the purification because as the crystals form, they select the correct molecules which fit into the crystal lattice and ignore the wrong molecules.* This is of course not a perfect process, but it does increase the purity of the final product.

The *polarity* of a molecule greatly affects its *physical properties,* such as melting point, boiling point, and solubility. In general, polar molecules have much higher melting and boiling points than nonpolar molecules of a similar molar mass. A simple illustration of this point is water and methane: water, a polar molecule, has a boiling point of 100 °C, while methane, a nonpolar molecule whose molecular mass is roughly the same as water, has a boiling point of −164 °C. A change from a nonpolar compound to a polar compound results in a difference in boiling point of more than 260 °C!

What accounts for these vast differences in the physical properties between polar and nonpolar molecules? If one considers the magnet analogy applied to polar compounds on a molecular scale, things begin to make sense. The process of melting occurs when molecules, stacked on top of one another in a crystal solid, are heated. As the temperature rises, the molecules gain enough energy to break free of each other, and thus the solid changes to a liquid. If one continues to heat the liquid, the molecules, which are still attracted to each other but slightly mobile, begin to move faster and faster in the liquid phase. When the temperature rises high enough, the molecules gain enough energy to break free of the attractions between the molecules and become a gas (boiling). As previously stated, polar molecules tend to stick more strongly to each other, so they require more energy, or a higher temperature, to separate, giving a higher melting and boiling point.

Polarity also affects *solubility* in solvents. Solvents range from polar to nonpolar. Polar solvents include water, methanol, ethanol, and acetic acid. Moderately polar solvents include dichloromethane, chloroform, tetrahydrofuran, acetone, ethyl acetate, and ether, while hexane, pentane, benzene, and toluene are nonpolar solvents. Due to the intermolecular attractive forces, polar compounds will be soluble in polar solvents, while nonpolar compounds will be soluble in nonpolar solvents. As far as solubility is concerned, the rule *"like dissolves like"* often applies. As an example, 1,1,2,2–tetrabromoethane is insoluble in water but very soluble in ether, while malonic acid ($HOOC–CH_2–COOH$) is soluble in water and alcohol, but insoluble in benzene.

The *solubility* of a compound in the solvent used for a recrystallization is important. In the ideal case, the solvent will completely dissolve the compound to be purified at high temperature, usually the boiling point of the solvent, and the compound will be completely insoluble in that solvent at room temperature or at 0 °C. In addition the impurity would be either completely insoluble in the particular solvent at the high temperature, or very soluble in the solvent at low temperature. In the former case, the impurity could be filtered off at high temperature, while in the latter case the impurity would completely stay in solution upon cooling. In the real world, this will never happen, and recrystallization is a technique that has to be practiced and perfected; therefore, this lab.

A pure organic solid has a fixed *melting point*. The purity of a sample can be judged by its melting point. The more depressed the melting point is compared to the reported literature value, the more impurity has been incorporated in the crystals. This phenomenon is called *melting point depression*.

Based on this phenomenon, we can use the melting point of a mixture to establish the identity of a sample. This procedure is called *mixed melting point determination*. A typical situation is as follows: a compound X is suspected of being identical to one of two substances, A and B. All three compounds have approximately the same melting point. Mixtures of about equal amounts of two are prepared and the melting points of these mixtures are determined. If A and X are identical, the melting point of the mixture of A and X will have the same melting point as the pure substances, apart from slight differences due to impurities specific to a certain sample. If A and X are different from each other, the melting point of their mixture will be significantly lower than that of either A or X.

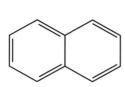

naphthalene

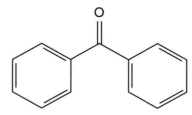

benzophenone

Aim of the Experiment

- Purification of two solids using recrystallization.

- Determine the identity of the compounds using melting point.

- Learn about the use of mixed melting points.

Learning Objectives

- Understand the factors that govern solubility.

- Understand the logic of the recrystallization process.

- Learn how to remove impurities from a solid compound.

Required Reading

- Measurement of weight and volume

- Heating and cooling methods

- Filtration

- Recrystallization

- Melting point

Safety Considerations

None of the chemicals used in this lab are particularly hazardous. Due caution should always be applied when dealing with any chemicals. Methanol and petroleum ether are very flammable.

Procedures

Two recrystallizations which simulate commonly encountered situations will be performed. Crude naphthalene contains a colored impurity with a higher solubility in the recrystallization solvent than pure naphthalene, and crude benzophenone contains an impurity that is less soluble in the recrystallization solvent than benzophenone itself. In addition the phenomenon of the mixed melting point will be illustrated by taking a mixed melting point of benzoic acid and 2-naphthol.

1. Naphthalene from Methanol

In this case the impurity deliberately added to naphthalene is colored and is more soluble than the desired product. To remove such impurities, the entire sample is dissolved and the material of interest is crystallized from the solvent, while the impurities should remain in solution. A colored impurity was selected to make it possible to visually monitor its removal from the colorless naphthalene. The color remaining after recrystallization is due primarily to impurity on the surface of the crystals. This may be largely removed by washing the crystals (while on the Hirsch funnel) with a small amount of cold solvent. Such washing of crystals is common practice.

Be sure your glassware is dry. If wet, rinse it with acetone and let the remaining acetone evaporate.

Use about 300 mg of crude naphthalene[1] and determine the amount of methanol solvent that is necessary by slowly dissolving the sample in hot solvent in a beaker placed on the hot plate (medium setting).[2] Once the material is dissolved, allow the material to slowly cool to room temperature. Then cool with an ice bath. Vacuum filter using the Hirsch funnel, wash with small amounts of cold solvent to remove any colored impurities clinging to the surface of the crystals. Leaving the Hirsch funnel setup connected to the house vacuum will dry the crystals. Determine the melting point of the impure starting material sample and of your crystals. Weigh the purified sample, and determine the % recovery.

2. Benzophenone from Petroleum Ether

(Petroleum ether is a mixture of hydrocarbons with a boiling point range 35–40 degrees)

In the benzophenone case, the deliberately added impurity is also colored, but less soluble in petroleum ether than benzophenone itself. The trick is to add just enough hot solvent to dissolve the desired material, while leaving the impurity behind as a solid. *Do not try to add enough solvent to dissolve the impurity,* or you will have to boil off a very large amount of solvent to recover your pure benzophenone.

Weigh out approximately 250 mg of impure benzophenone.[3] Grind up the sample using a mortar and pestle if necessary.

Place the impure benzophenone in a 25 or 50 mL beaker and add approximately 7–8 mL of preheated solvent.[4] Heat the mixture on the hot plate until the solvent boils and the benzophenone crystals dissolve. If necessary, add small quantities of petroleum ether with a pipet until all the white benzophenone is dissolved.

Filter the hot solution using gravity filtration (no vacuum) or decant the solution.[5] Cool the benzophenone solution to room temperature, and then in an ice bath. Filter the obtained crystals using a Hirsch funnel and wash the flask and crystals with a small amount of cold petroleum ether. Dry the crystals on the funnel by using the vacuum to pull air over them for at least 5 minutes. Determine the melting point of the impure starting material sample and of your crystals. Weigh your purified sample, and calculate the % recovery.

3. Mixed Melting Points Determination

To demonstrate the phenomenon of melting point depression, mix a few mg of benzoic acid with an equal amount of 2-naphthol by grinding them up in a mortar. Determine the melting point. Compare the melting point of the mixture with the melting point of the pure substances.

Report

For each recrystallization the following should be included in your report: exact amount of crude starting material, identify the solvent and amount used, the yield of pure material recovered (% recovery), the melting point of the impure and pure material.

For the mixed melting point experiments: the melting point of each mixture and the melting points of pure benzoic acid and 2-naphthol.

Notes

1. You have to know exactly how much naphthalene you are starting with, but it should not be exactly 300 mg. The exact amount is necessary to calculate the % recovery after purification.

2. It will take about 7–9 mL of methanol to dissolve this amount of naphthalene. Don't be too paranoid about adding too much solvent, because it can be evaporated off if necessary.

3. While you do not need to weigh out exactly 250 mg, you should know the exact weight of material you use in this experiment to calculate the % recovery at the end of the purification.

4. You can gently preheat petroleum ether in a beaker placed on the hot plate (medium to low setting).

5. If the crystals "crash out" during the filtration, reheat the solution to redissolve the crystals.

Discussion

• Explain the basic logic of a recrystallization procedure. What happens at the molecular level?

• Explain the difference in recrystallization procedures used depending on the compound to be purified and the nature of the contaminants.

• Defend the choice of solvents for each of the two procedures.

• Explain the % recovery you obtained.

• Discuss the principle of mixed melting point and how it can be a useful technique.

Questions

1. How would a mixture of naphthalene and benzophenone behave on a TLC plate with hexanes/acetone as the eluent? Compare the polarity of these two compounds.

2. Outline the most commonly used procedure for the purification of an impure solid material using the technique of recrystallization.

3. Why is acetone such a popular solvent? Point out one drawback in terms of safety considerations.

4. Your final product might be impure since you suspect decomposition might have occurred. When determining the melting point of your product, what are you looking for?

5. Why is it important to use a minimal amount of hot solvent during a recrystallization? What would happen if you used too much solvent while dissolving your solid?

6. Why is it important to cool the dissolved product/solvent mixture slowly during a recrystallization?

7. Discuss the melting point range characteristics of a pure and an impure sample.

8. An accurate melting point range can be obtained by heating the sample quickly just as well as if obtained by allowing the temperature to rise slowly. True or False? Explain.

9. What is the first indication of a sample melting in the melting point tube?

10. Suppose your sample melts before you are ready to record the melting point. Should you a) cool the capillary and redetermine the mp or b) begin with a fresh sample? Explain.

5a

Isolation of Caffeine from Tea or Coffee

Caffeine

Pyrimidines and purines are heterocyclic ring[1] compounds found in deoxyribonucleic acids (DNA) and ribonucleic acids (RNA), the complex molecules that transmit genetic information and mediate the synthesis of proteins in cells. The pyrimidine and purine bases found in DNA and RNA are shown below.

Other purine bases occur in nature, such as xanthine, hypoxanthine, and uric acid, which are products of the metabolism of the purine bases adenine and guanine. In humans, urea is a product of the metabolism of purine bases. Caffeine is a methylated form of xanthine and is a powerful stimulant of the central nervous system. Caffeine is classified as an *alkaloid*, a class of naturally occurring compounds containing nitrogen and acting as amine bases. Pure caffeine was first isolated from coffee in 1821 by the French chemist Pierre Jean Robiquet.

Caffeine is best known as a stimulant of the central nervous system and the skeletal muscles. This results in increased alertness, ability to stay awake, and increased capacity for thinking. It is therefore the main ingredient of such over-the-counter drugs as No-Doz. Xanthines have a variety of other effects: they can act as diuretics (induce urination and reduce water-retention problems), myocardial (heart muscle) stimulants, bronchodilators (relax the bronchioles of the lungs), and vasodilators

Pyrimidine Bases

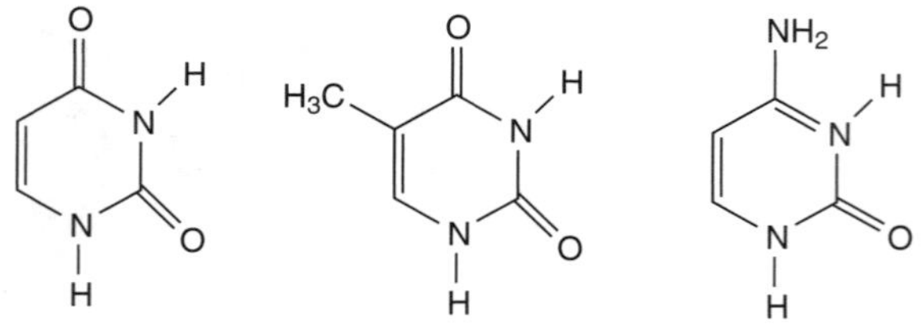

| Uracil (RNA) | Thymine (DNA) | Cytosine (DNA, RNA) |

Purine Bases

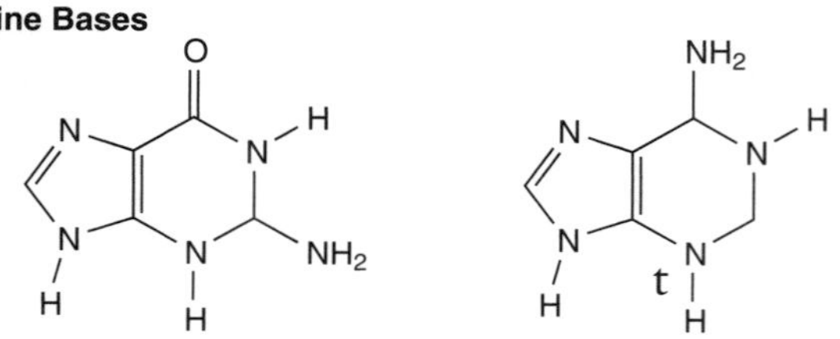

| Guanine (RNA, DNA) | Adenine (RNA, DNA) |

| xanthine | caffeine (tea, coffee, cola nuts) |

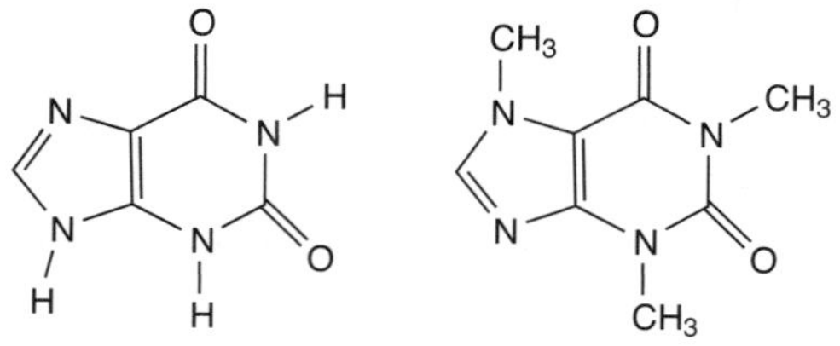

(relax blood vessels). Caffeine interferes with glycogen breakdown, and mainly inhibits both liver and skeletal muscle cells' ability to use glycogen. This inability to use glycogen has two main effects: liver cells can't use glycogen to release glucose into the bloodstream, and skeletal muscles are forced to use a different source of energy.

Decaffeinated coffee, in which the caffeine content of the beans has been reduced from ~5% to between 0.03 – 1.2%, is obtained by extracting the caffeine from coffee beans. Methylene chloride, CH_2Cl_2, was once used for this purpose. The solvent containing the caffeine was then drained off, and the beans were steamed to remove any residual solvent. However, concerns about the safety of the coffee with residual traces of methylene chloride prompted a change to the use of supercritical liquid carbon dioxide.[2] Chloroform ($CHCl_3$) and carbon tetrachloride (CCl_4) are toxic and carcinogenic and, even though methylene chloride is considered safer, it should be used carefully.

Background

Caffeine will be isolated and purified by sublimation. A sequence of extractions has to be performed because tea leaves are obviously a very complex mixture. All the known ingredients have to be considered, and based on solubilities and acidity/basicity of the different components, an extraction scheme has to be devised. Tea leaves consist of the following components:

- **cellulose** is the principal structural material of all plant cells. Cellulose is one of the most abundant organic compounds in the biosphere. Some 10^{15} kg of cellulose is synthesized and degraded on earth each year! It is an unbranched polymer of glucose residues and forms very long, straight chains, resulting in fibers with high tensile strength. Very efficient intra- and intermolecular H-bonding makes cellulose virtually insoluble in water.
- **tannins** are a family of compounds containing phenolic components (phenol = hydroxybenzene) and have molecular weights between 500 and 3,000. They are used to "tan" leather because they precipitate alkaloids and proteins from aqueous solutions. They have complicated structures and can be divided into two main classes, hydrolyzable and non-hydrolyzable tannins. The former are esters of glucose and gallic acid, while the latter are condensation polymers of catechin. The ester groups in the hydrolyzable tannins can be partially hydrolyzed in hot water, resulting in glucose and gallic acid. The common feature of all tannins is the acidity of the phenol groups, which means they will react with bases, such as sodium carbonate, to form water-soluble sodium salts.

glucose   cellulose

glucose   gallic acid   catechin

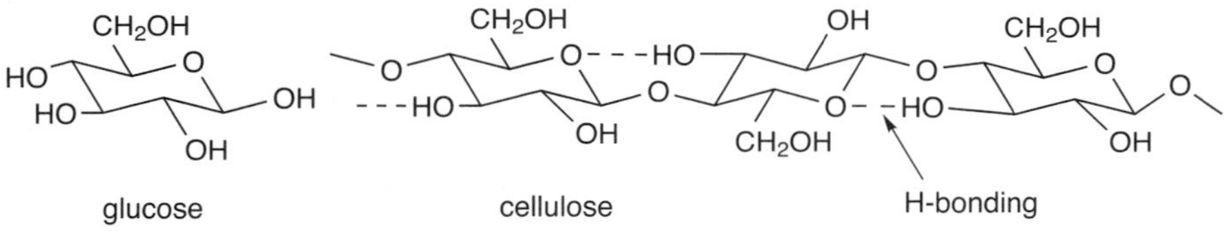

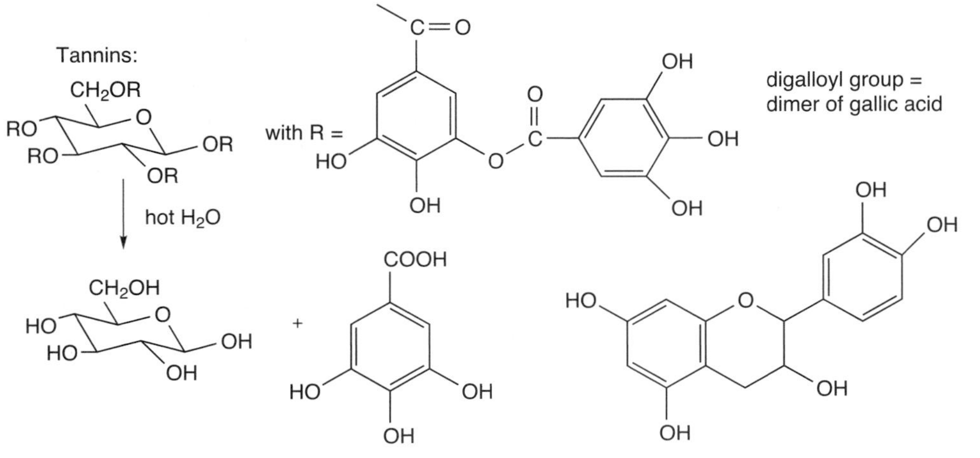

- **flavonoid pigments and chlorophylls** and related oxidation products give tea its color. Only the chlorophylls are soluble in methylene chloride.

- **caffeine** is the ingredient of interest for this experiment. It is soluble in hot water, and very soluble in methylene chloride.

According to the National Soft Drink Association, the following is the caffeine content in mg per 12 oz can of soda:

Afri-Cola	100.0
Jolt	71.2
Sugar-Free Mr. Pibb	58.8
Mountain Dew	55.0
Diet Mountain Dew	55.0
Mello Yellow	52.8
Tab	46.8
Coca-Cola	45.6
Diet Cola	45.6
Shasta Cola	44.4
Shasta Cherry Cola	44.4
Shasta Diet Cola	44.4
Mr. Pibb	40.8
OK Soda	40.5
Dr Pepper	39.6
Pepsi Cola	37.2
Aspen	36.0
Diet Pepsi	35.4
RC Cola	36.0
Diet RC	36.0
Diet Rite	36.0
Canada Dry Cola	30.0
Canada Dry Diet Cola	1.2
7 Up	0

A 7 oz cup of coffee has the following caffeine (mg) amounts, according to Bunker and McWilliams in *J. Am. Diet.* 74:28–32, 1979:

Drip	115–175
Espresso 1 serving (1.5–2 oz)	100
Brewed	80–135
Instant	65–100
Decaf, brewed	3–4
Decaf, instant	2–3
Tea, iced (12 oz.)	70
Tea, brewed, imported	60
Tea, brewed, U.S.	40
Tea, instant	30
Mate	25–150

The variability in the amount of caffeine in a cup of coffee or tea is relatively large even if prepared by the same person using the same equipment and ingredients day after day.[3]

Based on these solubility data, an extraction scheme can be devised. Hot water will extract the following out of the tea leaves or ground coffee beans: caffeine, tannins (which will partially hydrolyze in the process), and some pigments. Treatment with base will convert all acidic materials to their respective salts. Extraction of the basic aqueous solution with methylene chloride will extract out only caffeine and possibly some chlorophylls. The crude caffeine can then be purified by sublimation.

Required Reading
- Sublimation
- Extractions
- Drying agents

Aim of the Experiment
- Isolate caffeine from tea of coffee.
- Purify isolated caffeine by sublimation.

Learning Objectives
- Apply a complex extraction procedure to isolate active ingredients isolated from natural products.
- Learn how to perform a sublimation procedure to purify a solid.

Procedure
Heat ~10 mL of water in a small beaker to almost boiling. Place the tea bag (2.265 g of tea per bag) or an individual coffee bag (5.595 g of coffee) in the water so as to be completely submerged and heat for ~15 minutes.[4] Transfer all the liquid to a centrifuge tube, pressing all the water out of the tea or coffee bag. Repeat the extraction with an additional 4–6 mL of water and add the extract to the centrifuge tube. While the solution is still warm, add 1.0 g of potassium carbonate (K_2CO_3)[5] and cap the tube. Shake until the carbonate dissolves. Cool to room temperature. Add 3 mL of methylene chloride (dichloromethane) and shake the mixture for one minute.[6] Centrifuge the mixture for 2–3 minutes to break the emulsion and to separate the layers.

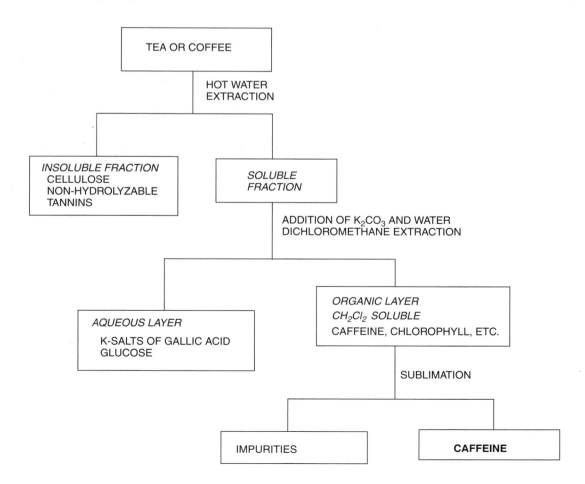

Remove the organic layer with a pipet,[7,8] and transfer it to a test tube. Repeat the extraction with 3 mL methylene chloride and combine both organic fractions. Dry over anhydrous sodium sulfate.[9] Transfer the dried organic fraction to a tared sublimation tube (test tube with a side arm) using a pipet, and evaporate the solvent by blowing air over the solution. Cool the residue as soon as the solvent has evaporated. Weigh the crude yield of caffeine.

The crude caffeine will be purified by sublimation using the test tube setup described in *Making the Connections*. Preheat the thermowell or heating mantle to 200 °C. Assemble the sublimation apparatus using the test tube containing the crude caffeine. Apply vacuum first. If you are certain a good vacuum has been obtained, place ice water into the inner tube, and then heat the sublimation apparatus. The sample should sublime very quickly; within a few minutes white crystals will collect on the cold inner tube. Remove the sublimator from the thermowell, then pipet out the cold water while the vacuum is still being applied.[10] When the apparatus is at room temperature, gently disconnect the vacuum hose and carefully remove the inner tube. These crystals are very fragile and could fall back into the tube. Scrape the sublimed caffeine onto a tared watch glass or weighing paper. Determine the yield of caffeine. Determine the melting point.

Calculate the weight percentage recovery of pure caffeine from the crude caffeine and from the tea leaves or coffee. Compare the amount of caffeine you obtained with the amount isolated by another student who used tea if you used coffee, or vice versa.

Record an IR spectrum if your sample is large enough.

Notes

1. Heterocyclic rings are rings containing atoms other than carbon; for example, the ring in caffeine contains a nitrogen atom.

2. The solvent properties of a supercritical liquid are between those of gas and liquid. The supercritical fluid phase of CO_2 is the phase above the critical point. In a phase diagram, when you move up the liquid-gas boundary (increasing temperature and pressure), a point is reached above which the two phases coexist, this is the critical point. Above this temperature only one phase exists, no matter what the pressure. For CO_2 the critical point is at 31.3 °C and 72.9 atm. The density and viscosity of a supercritical liquid are between those of a gas and liquid, as is its ability to act as a solvent.

3. Reference: *Variability in caffeine consumption from coffee and tea: Possible significance for epidemiological studies* by B. Stavric, R. Klassen, B. Watkinson, K. Karpinski, R. Stapley, and P. Fried in *Foundations of Chemical Toxicology*, Volume 26, number 2, pp. 111–118, 1988 and an easy-to-read overview, *Looking for the Perfect Brew* by S. Eisenberg, *Science News*, Volume 133, April 16, 1988, pp. 252–253.

4. Gently push the bag around several times to optimize the extraction of the tea or coffee. Keep water volume constant by adding small portions as it evaporates. Add more water if necessary.

5. Potassium carbonate is a base, which will convert all available carboxylic acid functionalities (–COOH) to their potassium salts (–COO⁻ K⁺) and make these compounds water soluble.

6. Pressure might build up in the centrifuge tube. Carefully vent the tube several times during this extraction procedure to release the pressure, but don't let the liquid squirt out.

7. Squeeze the pipet bulb before lowering the pipet into the liquid.

8. You will need to know the density of methylene chloride to decide which layer is the organic layer and which one is the aqueous layer. *It is good practice never to dispose of any fractions until you are sure the extracted material is really where you think it ought to be.*

9. Add a small amount of granular sodium sulfate (several spatula tips) and swirl the mixture. If all sodium sulfate clumps, add some additional drying agent. Let stand for ~10 minutes, shaking the test tube occasionally. Water and dichloromethane don't mix; therefore as long as you see droplets, water is still present.

10. If the vacuum is released before the ice water is removed, water will condense on the cold finger, thereby contaminating, and maybe even dissolving, the caffeine.

Discussion

•   Discuss the extraction procedure used to obtain crude caffeine. In particular,

   •   How is the first step the same/different from brewing coffee?

   •   Explain the use of acid–base chemistry to accomplish the desired result.

   •   Explain the use of organic solvents and water.

•   Explain the sublimation technique: Why use a vacuum? Why a cold finger? etc.

•   How successful was your experiment? Explain.

Questions

1. Would the methylene chloride layer be above or below the aqueous layer in today's experiment? Justify your answer.

2. Why is potassium carbonate used in the isolation of caffeine? Be specific as to the chemical species the carbonate may act on.

3. Why was sodium sulfate used?

4. After introducing 1.0 g of potassium carbonate into the centrifuge tube containing the hot water extract, it was capped, shaken, and then cooled to room temperature. Following this, roughly 3 mL of dichloromethane was added and the mixture shaken for one minute. Why wasn't the dichloromethane placed in the centrifuge tube with the carbonate and the warm extract in one step? Hint: check the boiling points.
    Where do the carboxylic acids end up?

5. Define sublimation. Explain, using a phase diagram.

6. Why is it important to add ice water to the cold finger *after* the vacuum has been turned on in your sublimation apparatus?

7. Draw and label the parts of a sublimation apparatus.

8. Draw an approximate phase diagram for caffeine. Label the axes and the phases (g), (l), and (s). Indicate the phase changes: sublimation, deposition, evaporation, condensation, melting, and freezing. Explain why we use vacuum for the sublimation.

9. If a cup of tea (100 mL) contains 40 mg of caffeine, what is the molar concentration of caffeine in tea?

Hydrogenation of a Fatty Acid

A fatty acid is a compound containing a long hydrocarbon chain and a terminal carboxylic acid group (–COOH). Fatty acids are building blocks for phospholipids and glycolipids; they are fuel molecules; they modify proteins by providing them with an anchor to cell membranes; and fatty acid derivatives serve as hormones and intracellular messengers. Fatty acids are stored in the body as triglycerides, namely as esters of glycerol $HO–CH_2–CH(OH)–CH_2–OH$. Fatty acids can be either fully saturated or contain one or more unsaturation in the hydrocarbon chain. Fatty acids in biological systems usually contain an even number of carbons, between 14 and 24. The 16– and 18–carbon fatty acids are the most common, and they are almost always unbranched.

From the table we can deduce several important facts about the physical properties of fatty acids, namely unsaturated fatty acids (with double bonds) have lower melting points than their saturated counterparts, the greater the degree of unsaturation, the lower the melting point, and the longer the chain, the higher the melting point. We should also point out that the double bonds in fatty acid are almost always Z (cis); the E isomer is rare.

Linoleic and linolenic fatty acids (see table) are the only fatty acids known to be essential for the complete nutrition of many species of animals, including humans. They are used to make prostaglandins,

Number of Carbons	Double Bonds	Structure	Name	Melting Point (° C)
12	0	$CH_3(CH_2)_{10}COOH$	lauric acid	44
14	0	$CH_3(CH_2)_{12}COOH$	myristic acid	58
16	0	$CH_3(CH_2)_{14}COOH$	palmitic acid	63
18	0	$CH_3(CH_2)_{16}COOH$	stearic acid	70
20	0	$CH_3(CH_2)_{18}COOH$	arachidic acid	77
22	0	$CH_3(CH_2)_{20}COOH$	behenic acid	80
24	0	$CH_3(CH_2)_{22}COOH$	lignoceric acid	122
16	1	$CH_3(CH_2)_5CH=CH(CH_2)_7COOH$	palmitoleic acid	−1
18	1	$CH_3(CH_2)_7CH=CH(CH_2)_7COOH$	oleic acid	16
18	2	$CH_3(CH_2)_4(CH=CHCH_2)_2(CH_2)_7COOH$	linoleic acid	−5
18	3	$CH_3CH_2(CH=CHCH_2)_3(CH_2)_7COOH$	linolenic acid	−11
20	4	$CH_3CH_2(CH=CHCH_2)_4(CH_2)_7COOH$	arachidonic acid	−49

thromboxanes, and leukotrienes, compounds which are involved in physiological processes in the body such as inflammatory response involving the joints (rheumatoid arthritis) and skin, production of pain and fever, regulation of blood pressure and blood clotting, decreased gastric acid secretion, induction of labor and delivery, and regulation of the sleep/wake cycle. So you need to consume these fatty acids in your diet to obtain these highly necessary compounds!

The fatty acids occur as the triglyceride in most naturally occurring fats and oils. The different kinds of fats contain different proportions of these fatty acids in the triglyceride esters. For example, olive oil contains approximately 85 % of oleic acid, while palm oil contains ~40 % palmitic acid and ~43 % oleic acid and coconut oil contains 45 % lauric acid.

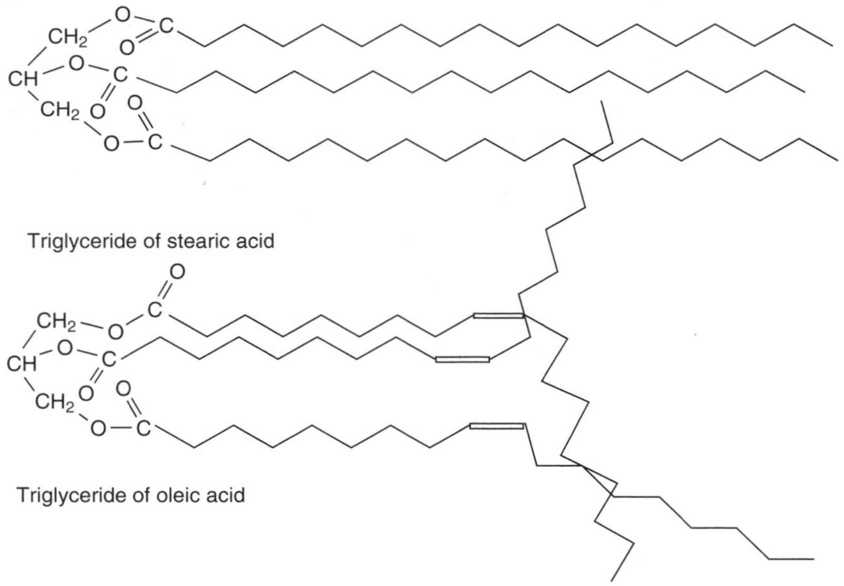

Triglyceride of stearic acid

Triglyceride of oleic acid

Safety Considerations

Hydrogen is a highly flammable gas. Absolutely no flames will be allowed in the lab.

The catalyst Pd/C is also flammable; chlorinated solvents "poison" this catalyst and render it inactive.

Be sure to wear your goggles at all times, because minor "explosions" can occur while handling the hydrogen.

The physical properties of the fatty acids illustrate their behavior in the human body. The more saturated a fatty acid, the easier the triglycerides will stack and build up in the body, while the unsaturation, the cis (Z) double bond, provides a kink in the long hydrocarbon chain that somewhat inhibits the buildup of the triglycerides. As stated above, olive oil is mostly unsaturated, while both palm and coconut oil contain a large proportion of saturated fatty acid, making these two much less healthy than olive oil.

Conversion of oils to fats is a major industry. In the process, called "hardening," unsaturated hydrocarbon chains are converted to their fully or partially saturated analogs. This will result in a higher melting point; thus conversion of liquids to solids becomes possible. Or in common words, they are converting oils into semisolid margarine, the consistency of which

can be regulated by the extent of saturation. The chemical reaction behind this conversion is simple hydrogen addition to a double bond, or hydrogenation. And this is exactly the reaction we will perform in this experiment. Liquid methyl oleate, with one double bond, will be converted by you to solid methyl stearate, its fully saturated analog.

Hydrogenation is a very slow reaction, unless it is catalyzed. Metal catalysts are most often used, and to make handling of these small amounts easier they are supported on some inert material, usually charcoal. Common catalysts are Raney Nickel (Ni/C), Pt/C, and Pd/C. These catalysts obviously do not dissolve in organic solvents, and they are present as a suspended solid in the reaction mixture. These are thus *heterogeneous* reactions, in which not all reaction partners are in the same phase. In *homogeneous* reactions, all reagents are dissolved in one solvent.

Electrophilic addition to double bonds proceeds much faster than hydrogenation. Addition of bromine to a C=C bond is very fast in polar solvent, resulting in a dibromide. The interesting thing about this reaction is that it can be used to test for unsaturations. A bromine solution in dichloromethane or carbon tetrachloride is brown in color. The test solution will go colorless if C=C bonds are present in a compound, because the bromine will react and add to the double bond.

Required Reading
- Hydrogenation in Organic Chemistry textbook.

Aim of the Experiment
- Perform a synthetic organic reaction, namely a hydrogenation.

- Test for unsaturation.

Learning Objectives
- Introduction to fatty acids and the structure of fats.

- Observe the relationship between structure, in this case unsaturation and stereochemistry around a double bond, and physical properties.

- Perform an organic reaction and work up the reaction.

- Observe the effect of catalysis on a reaction.

- Calculate percent yield of a synthetic reaction.

- Differentiate between homogeneous and heterogeneous reaction conditions.

- Learn a qualitative test for unsaturation.

Procedure
This hydrogenation is the first preparative organic reaction of this course. The reaction is the hydrogenation of methyl oleate to form methyl stearate. The change in physical properties between the starting material and product is very obvious, showing a reaction has taken place.

The hydrogenation apparatus consists of a round-bottom flask with a magnetic stirrer capped by a balloon filled with hydrogen gas.

The methyl oleate used in this experiment is only 70 % pure; the other 30 % are unreactive saturated impurities which do not interfere with the reaction.[1]

Add ~0.5 g of methyl oleate to a 10 mL round-bottom flask.[2] Add about 3 mL of methanol. When everything is ready for quick assembly, ask your TA to introduce about 15 mg of 10 % Pd/C catalyst to the reaction mixture.[3] Place the balloon filled with hydrogen on the reaction vessel and start the stirrer. Heat the reaction flask to 40 °C. Stir for 45–60 minutes. The black catalyst color will eventually change to grey[4] and the volume of the balloon might have decreased.

Work-up
Remove the balloon, add 0.5 mL of dichloromethane[5] and heat the mixture to dissolve all product. Add a spatula full of Celite.[6] Filter the hot methyl stearate/Celite slurry as fast as possible, using a Hirsch funnel, and wash with a minimal amount of methanol. Cool the filtered solution; use an ice bath if necessary. Collect the crystals by filtration, dry the crystals, weigh and determine the melting point (lit. 39 °C).

Record the infrared spectrum of methyl stearate. Compare it to the spectrum of methyl oleate.

Test both methyl oleate and your product for unsaturation with a dilute solution of bromine in dichloromethane. Bromine will readily add to any aliphatic double bond present in a compound. Bromine has a brown color, so when it reacts the solution will go from brown to colorless. The brown color persists with the fully saturated compounds.

In your report, don't forget to calculate the percent yield.[7]

Notes

1. These % values are weight %.

2. Weigh the flask first empty, then add about 0.5 mL methyl oleate to the flask using a syringe and reweigh. Determine the exact weight of the starting material.

3. The catalyst is highly pyrophoric and should not be exposed to air. The catalyst should remain covered with methanol at all times. The TA should wash down any catalyst clinging to the side of the flask with a little squirt of methanol. Do not start the magnetic stirrer until after the system is closed under hydrogen atmosphere.

4. Methyl stearate has limited solubility in methanol and will start to precipitate out as the reaction proceeds.

5. The dichloromethane serves two different purposes: it poisons the catalyst, i.e., renders it inactive, and it is also a very good solvent for the stearate.

6. Celite is also called Filter Aid or diatomaceous earth, and is a very fine material obtained from the microscopic shells of dead diatoms, a phytoplankton. Celite is a help to filter very finely divided material, in this case the catalyst, and it does not clog the filter paper.

7. Remember that the starting material only contains 70 % of methyl oleate.

Discussion

- Explain the reaction conditions, i.e., why is the reaction run the way it is? Don't just copy the procedure, but explain.

- Explain the logic of the work-up procedure. What do we do with the reaction mixture once the reaction is finished? And why?

- Discuss the difference in reaction rates between hydrogen and bromine addition. Why do we need a catalyst for the hydrogenation?

Questions

1. You have just hydrogenated an unsaturated fatty acid and made a saturated fatty acid. The resulting product is crystalline. Give three methods that could help you prove the hydrogenation was successful.

2. You hydrogenate benzene using Rh/C and hydrogen gas similar to your lab procedure. Your balloon contains 15 L of H_2 gas. If you started with 0.72 g of benzene, what is your theoretical yield of cyclohexane? If you obtain 0.72 g of cyclohexane, what is your percent yield? How much hydrogen (volume) did you use?

3. Cyclohexene has two degrees of unsaturation, but one mole of cyclohexene will react with only one mole of H_2. True or False? Why?

4. Experience has shown that an alkene is best characterized by its property of decolorizing both a solution of bromine in CCl_4 and a cold, dilute, neutral permanganate solution. (Baeyer test)
   a. What does a positive bromine test look like? What is it a test for? Demonstrate on methyl oleate.
   b. How would the Baeyer reagent react with methyl oleate? How can the reaction be monitored? ($KMnO_4$ is purple and MnO_2 is brown)

5. Without any analytical tools, how can you determine that a particular compound is an unsaturated compound?

6. A particular compound with a formula $C_{10}H_{16}$ takes up one mole of H_2 on catalytic hydrogenation. Give a possible structure for it. If it takes up two moles of hydrogen on reduction, give one structure that fits this information.

7. Give the reagents and the principal organic product(s) for the following problem:
   a. 80 g of 1,3–cyclohexadiene was reacted with one mole of hydrogen gas.
   b. the product(s) from part (a) was(were) treated with bromine.

8. Cyclohexene (5 mL, d = 0.811) is hydrogenated using H_2 and Raney Ni. After distillation, you obtain 3.25 g of cyclohexane. Calculate the % yield.

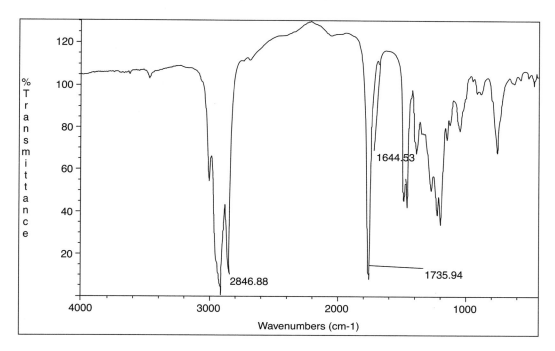

IR spectrum of methyl oleate

Fischer Esterification

Carboxylic esters are widely found in natural compounds and often have pleasant odors. Many esters are used in the flavoring and perfume industry, and they are commonly added to foods and beverages to produce "fruity" flavors. Many times these esters are not found in nature, but mimic natural flavors. A flavor formula usually contains a mixture of 10 or more components to achieve a certain flavor/smell. Very seldom is just one ester sufficient to accomplish a "natural" flavor. Some common flavors are shown here.

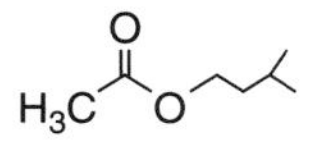

isopentyl acetate
(banana)

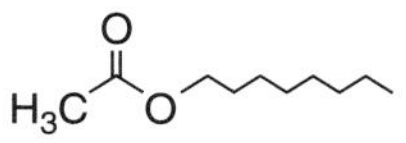

octyl acetate
(orange)

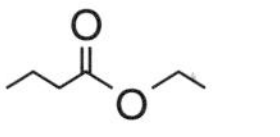

ethyl butanoate
(pineapple)

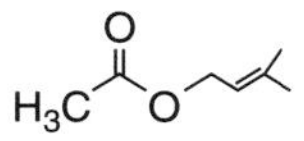

isopentenyl acetate
("juicy fruit")

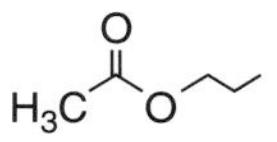

propyl acetate
(pear)

In contrast to the carboxylic esters, the carboxylic acids from which they are derived usually have very unpleasant smells. This is again an example of a small variation in structure which results in a definite change in the perception of these compounds by the sensors in the nose.

$$CH_3-\overset{\displaystyle O}{\overset{\displaystyle \|}{C}}-OH \quad + \quad ROH \quad \underset{\xrightarrow{\hspace{1cm}}}{\overset{H_2SO_4}{\rightleftharpoons}} \quad CH_3-\overset{\displaystyle O}{\overset{\displaystyle \|}{C}}-O-R \quad + \quad H_2O$$

acetic acid   alcohol
(excess)

Carboxylic esters can be made by a variety of methods from the corresponding carboxylic acids. On paper the simplest method to synthesize an ester is to react a carboxylic acid with an alcohol. This reaction is named the Fischer esterification.[1]

The reaction of a carboxylic acid with an alcohol is an equilibrium, and therefore governed by the equilibrium constant. The equilibrium constant for esterifications with primary alcohols is usually very close to unity; e.g., the equilibrium constant for the reaction shown below for the synthesis of ethyl acetate is 3.38. The equilibrium should be shifted to the right, namely to completion, by applying Le Châtelier's principle.

$$K_{eq} = \frac{[ester]}{[acid][ROH]} = 3.38$$

According to Le Châtelier's principle, *a system at equilibrium adjusts so as to minimize any stress applied to it*. In the reaction of acetic acid and ethanol, the equilibrium can be shifted to the right by doing one of many things: either the concentration of acetic acid is increased, or the concentration of ethanol is increased, or ethyl acetate is somehow removed from the system, or water is somehow removed from the system. Either of the first two conditions is easily accomplished by adjusting the concentrations of the starting materials. Because ethyl acetate has a lower boiling point than water, we could distill out the ethyl acetate as it forms by critically controlling the temperature of the reaction. The last conditions, namely removing the water, could be accomplished if a drying agent, which will exclusively take the water out of the system, were added to the system, such as, for example, 4Å molecular sieves.

If you are interested, the mechanism for the Fischer esterification is discussed in great detail in your organic chemistry textbook. The reaction is catalyzed by the addition of an acid.

Required Reading
- Simple distillation

Aim of the Experiment
- Perform another synthetic organic reaction.

- Different acetates will be synthesized.

- The product will be identified by IR and NMR.

Learning Objectives
- Perform a synthesis reaction.

- Apply Le Châtelier's principle to an equilibrium reaction. The equilibrium will be controlled by the excess acetic acid.

- Use acid catalysis to enhance the reaction rate.

- Use an extraction procedure to isolate the product from the excess acid.

- Purify the product by distillation.

- Calculate percent yield of the reaction; the limiting reagent will have to be determined first.

- Observe the influence of structure on the smell of the compound.

Procedure

Specifically, acetic acid will be esterified with a variety of alcohols. The equilibrium will be controlled by using excess acetic acid, because it is cheaper than the alcohols and because it is more easily removed from the mixture after reaction. In the percent yield calculation, the limiting reagent will have to be determined first.

The following alcohols will be available for the reaction: 1-pentanol, 2-pentanol, isopentyl alcohol, hexyl alcohol, and 4-methyl-2-pentanol. You will use one of these according to your TA's instructions.

Weigh an empty 10 mL round-bottom flask. Place approximately 1.5 mL of the alcohol in the flask and reweigh the flask. Add ~ 3 mL glacial acetic acid[2, 3] (MW 60, d 1.06 g/mL). After placing a few boiling chips in the flask, add 2–3 drops of concentrated sulfuric acid. Assemble a reflux apparatus. Place the assembly in the heating mantle and heat to reflux for 60–70 minutes.[4]

Work-up

Cool the reaction mixture. While stirring, add slowly 2–3 mL of 5 % aqueous sodium bicarbonate, or more if needed. Stir until CO_2 formation ceases.[5] Transfer the reaction mixture to a centrifuge or test tube, shake it really hard, let it settle, and remove the lower aqueous layer with a Pasteur pipet. Centrifuge if necessary. Repeat the extraction of the organic layer with bicarbonate two more times. Remove as much of the water as possible with a Pasteur pipet, and add a small amount (a microspatula full) of granular sodium sulfate. Cap and let stand for 10–15 minutes.

Transfer the dry ester to a small round-bottom flask and add a boiling chip. Assemble a distillation apparatus using the Hickman stillhead. Place the distillation assembly in the heating mantle heated to ~180 °C, and distill the acetate.[6] Check and record the boiling point of the product by suspending a digital thermometer in the warm vapors during the distillation.[7] After the distillation, transfer the acetate to a tared vial, and weigh.

Obtain an IR spectrum of your product. Submit a sample for NMR analysis to your instructor.[8]

In your report, calculate % yield, and discuss the purity of your product as evidenced by the boiling point, the IR, and NMR spectrum (NMR will be discussed during the next lab). Also comment on the smell of your ester compared to the esters synthesized by your colleagues in the lab.

Notes

1. The most efficient method to synthesize a carboxylic ester is by reaction of the acid chloride derivative (or anhydride) with an alcohol. A similar method will be employed in the OFF experiment during the synthesis of an amide, in the second semester. Another method of synthesizing an ester is by treating an ester with an alcohol, in which the ester rest is exchanged. This is called a *transesterification* reaction and will be the subject of another lab next semester (FAME).

2. Glacial acetic acid is anhydrous acetic acid. The name comes from the cold effect it has on your skin if spilled. (Not a good idea.) The German name for acetic acid is *Eisessig*, literally ice acid.

3. The amount of acetic acid is not critical. The only requirement is that it be used in excess.

4. Reflux means heating the mixture to a temperature at which the solvent, or lowest boiling component of a mixture, boils and recondenses (turns liquid again) in the reflux condenser.

   Don't forget to circulate water through your condenser.

5. The excess acetic acid will be removed by extraction. Acetic acid is an acid, and reaction with a base, in this case sodium bicarbonate, will lead to the formation of a salt, which is very water soluble and rather insoluble in the organic phase. Acetic acid is thus removed from the organic phase, leaving only remaining alcohol and the reaction product in the organic phase, along with impurities.

$$CH_3COOH + NaHCO_3 \rightarrow$$
$$CH_3COONa + H_2O + CO_2\uparrow$$

6. It may be necessary to empty the Hickman stillhead during the distillation if too much material accumulates. Use a Pasteur pipet to remove the product through the side arm.

7. You have to hold the thermometer manually. Remember that you can never heat up a closed system. These tend to blow up!

8. Place two drops of the ester in a NMR tube. Don't worry if you don't see the product in the NMR tube. If you put it in there, it is in there! Your TA will add the solvent $CDCl_3$ and TMS standard.

Discussion

- Explain the reaction conditions, i.e., why is the reaction run the way it is?

- Explain the logic of the extraction procedure. What do we do with the reaction mixture once the reaction is finished? And why?

- Comment on the % yield you obtained.

- Discuss the purity and identification of your product as evidenced by the observed boiling point, IR spectrum, and NMR spectrum.

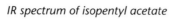

IR spectrum of isopentyl acetate

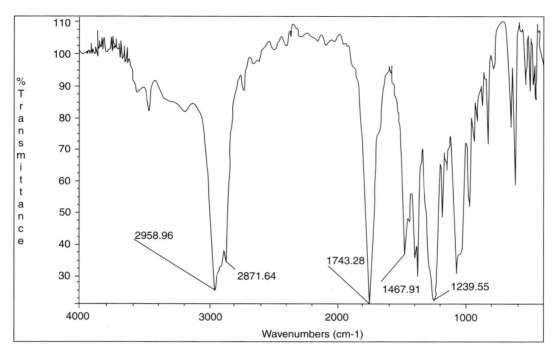

IR spectrum of impure isopentyl acetate (contains acetic acid)

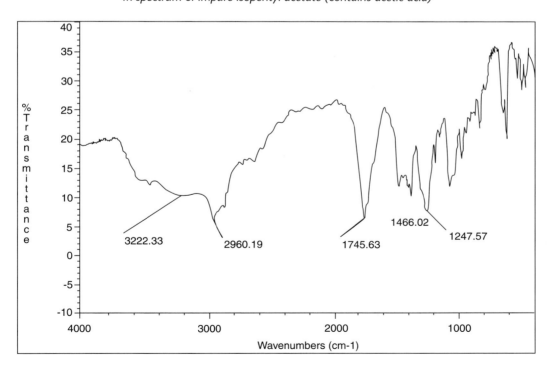

Questions

1. Assuming the difference in relative boiling points of methyl acetate (bp 57 °C) and 2-butanone (bp 80 °C) is caused by the difference in their dipole moments, predict which compound has the greater dipole moment. Use a vector analysis of bond dipoles to explain your answer.

2. Propionic acid and methyl acetate are isomers. Which has the higher boiling point and why? Which one would have the greater R_f value on TLC? Why?

3. Poly(ethylene terephthalate), which is the commonly used polyester Dacron, can be formed by an acid-catalyzed esterification between ethylene glycol ($HOCH_2CH_2OH$) and terephthalic acid ($HOOC-C_6H_4-COOH$, para isomer). Show the polymerization reaction.

4. How would you change the reaction conditions of acid-catalyzed esterification to favor ester hydrolysis rather than ester formation?

5. Give the structure of the product formed when adipic acid ($HOOC-(CH_2)_4-COOH$) is reacted with a large excess of 1–propanol with a sulfuric acid catalyst.

6. How many moles of isopentyl acetate are there in 1 g of isopentyl acetate?

7. How many moles of isopentyl acetate are there in 1 mL of isopentyl acetate?

8. Why is the reaction mixture extracted with sodium bicarbonate? Write out the reaction and explain why it is necessary to do this.

9. If 1 g of isopentyl alcohol is reacted with an excess acetic acid, and 1 mL of isopentyl acetate (d = 0.876) is obtained, what is the % yield?

8a

Nuclear Magnetic Resonance Spectroscopy

NMR is without a doubt the spectroscopic method most often used by organic chemists. It is an extremely versatile analysis method because it gives the chemist a lot of information about the number and type of atoms in a molecule, and their bonding patterns. In addition, results can be obtained in a relatively short time and without too much difficulty with modern instruments.

In this lab no practical laboratory work has to be performed. Instead the problem set has to be turned in to your TA. The problems are designed to give you information about NMR and to familiarize you with the practical side of this spectroscopic method. The basic principles of NMR will be explained in the lecture class. In this laboratory exercise more time is spent on the technique of solving spectra. What information can be obtained from the spectrum and how?

In this exercise it is important to show the "work" done. How did you arrive at your answer? Your TA has to be able to see how you solved the problems and will grade you accordingly.

In addition, you will receive the NMR spectrum of your previous lab. The TA will help you interpret this spectrum so that you can decide if you indeed obtained the correct product, and if it is pure.

Required Reading
- NMR spectroscopy

Aim of the Experiment
- Familiarize yourself with NMR spectroscopy.

- Solve NMR problems.

- Identify by NMR the product from the previous lab; i.e., the ester you obtained from the Fischer reaction.

Learning Objectives
- No practical lab work.

- Exercise in identification of organic compounds based on NMR.

- Learn how chemists confirm that they have obtained the product they expected.

Some Hints on How to Solve a NMR Spectrum

1. First try to get as much information as possible about the structure of the unknown from the molecular formula. From a cursory glance at the molecular formula, we can, of course, decide if the unknown is a pure hydrocarbon (contains only C and H), or if more functionalities are present. Is O present, or N, or a halogen?

    From the ratio of C to H, we can determine the *number of unsaturations* in the unknown. Alkanes have the general molecular formula C_nH_{2n+2} because each carbon will have two H plus the two hydrogens at the end of the linear hydrocarbon isomer. In a hydrocarbon, any less H will indicate sites of unsaturations, namely double (or triple) bonds or rings. Each unsaturation will

result in two less hydrogens in the molecular formula. Therefore, for a hydrocarbon, the following formula calculates the number of unsaturations:

$$\text{\# of unsaturations} = \#C + 1 - \tfrac{1}{2}\,(\#H)$$

in which #C is the number of carbon in the unknown, and #H is the number of hydrogens in the unknown sample.

As an example, a molecular formula of C_4H_6 indicates:

$$\text{\# of unsaturations} = \\ \#C + 1 - \tfrac{1}{2}\,(\#H) = 4 + 1 - \tfrac{1}{2}\,(6) = 2$$

therefore, C_4H_6 contains either two double bonds, e.g., 1,3–butadiene, or a ring and a double bond, e.g., cyclobutene.

When other elements are present, they also have to be taken into account. A **halogen** X, like Cl or Br, counts as a hydrogen. Therefore the formula becomes:

$$\text{\# of unsaturations} = \#C + 1 - \tfrac{1}{2}\,(\#H + \#X)$$

Oxygen is divalent and can be ignored in the calculation of the number of unsaturations. To satisfy yourself about this, you can calculate the molecular formulas of butane and diethyl ether, and calculate the number of unsaturations. Also compare acetone and allyl alcohol.

With **nitrogen**, things get a little bit more complex because it is trivalent. If a nitrogen is present in the MF, the formula becomes:

$$\text{\# of unsaturations} = \\ \#C + 1 - \tfrac{1}{2}(\#H + \#X - \#N)$$

The whole thing might seem rather complex, but will give you a lot of information about the molecule's structure. Remember the # of unsaturations gives you a total number of the double bonds **and** rings. Any molecule with 4 or more unsaturations will most likely be aromatic, and a glance at the NMR spectrum will tell you immediately if this is true (signals between δ 7–8 ppm).

Table of chemical shifts

Type of Proton	Chemical Shift δ (ppm)
TMS Standard	0
alkanes (C$\underline{H}_3$, C$\underline{H}_2$, C$\underline{H}$)	0.9 – 1.3
C$\underline{H}_x$–C=O	2 – 2.5
C$\underline{H}_x$–C=C	1.7 – 2
C$\underline{H}_x$–aromatic	2.3
–C$\underline{H}_x$–X (X = Cl, Br, I)	3 – 4
–C$\underline{H}_x$–O	3 – 4
$\underline{H}$–C=C	5 – 6
Aromatic $\underline{H}$	7 – 8
R–C$\underline{H}$=O	9 – 10
R–COO$\underline{H}$	10 – 15

For a more detailed table, consult Making the Connections.

2. The NMR spectrum will give us information as to how **many different kinds of protons** are present in the unknown. Equivalent protons will give the same signal. A first analysis of the spectrum should involve a determination of how many different signals are present. Be aware that a signal may be split into doublets, triplets, or more peaks, depending on the number of hydrogens on the neighboring carbon (see below), but a split signal is only one signal.

3. **Integration** of the signals will give you information about how many hydrogens a specific signal corresponds to. Remember that the integration will give you only a ratio of the number of hydrogens.

4. Armed with all this information, chemical shifts will have to be taken into account to determine the environment of the hydrogens. For example, a signal at δ 7.5 will most likely indicate aromatic hydrogens, while a singlet at δ 4 might mean a methyl ester.

5. The multiplicity of the signals gives information about the number of hydrogens on the neighboring carbon. A signal will be split into (n+1) peaks if there are n hydrogens on the neighboring carbon. A singlet implies that there are no hydrogens on the neighbor. This might mean many things; e.g., the carbon on which the hydrogens reside is next to a heteroatom such as O, or a quaternary carbon, or a carbon with three chlorines, or .... A doublet means that there is one hydrogen on the neighboring carbon, a triplet two, etc.

6. Combining all this information, like a puzzle, a structure can be proposed for the unknown.

Discussion
• No discussion on this one!

9a

Chirality, Gas Chromatography and Menthone

Enantiomers are stereoisomers that are related as two non-superimposable mirror images. The most common chiral center is a carbon substituted with four different substituents. The absolute structure of a chiral, or asymmetric center, is identified as either R or S. The rules to determine whether a chiral center is either R or S are amply explained in your organic chemistry textbook.

The word enantiomer describes a particular relationship between two molecules. A chiral molecule can have one, and only one, enantiomer. Two enantiomers will have many identical physical properties; for example, the melting point, boiling point, and density will be the same. The NMR spectra and IR spectra of the two enantiomers will also be identical. As to the properties which are related to the arrangement of atoms in space, there are striking differences.

The most obvious difference between two volatile enantiomers will be their odor. The odor of a compound greatly depends on its spatial shape. In "The Stereochemical Theory of Odor,"[1] Amoore postulates that there are seven basic odors, which correspond to specific shapes of molecules, and therefore only seven kinds of receptors in the nose. If the receptor sites are chiral, then enantiomers might have different odors.

Another property of chiral molecules is their ability to rotate plane-polarized light in opposite directions, therefore the name optically active compounds. Optical activity or rotation is measured by using a polarimeter, which measures the rotation of polarized light by means of two polarized filters.

Peppermint oil is a complex mixture of several natural products, some of which are optically active. It contains (–)-menthol and also the corresponding ketone (–)-menthone. The (–) sign indicates that a solution of either one of these compounds will rotate the light in a negative direction in a polarimeter. As you can see, menthol and menthone contain three and two chiral centers, respectively. The exact mirror image of each molecule will result in the opposite optical rotation.

If we analyze the structure of (–)- and (+)-menthone, we can see that the two enantiomers have the exact opposite structure in each of the chiral centers. However, if we only change one of the chiral centers, the resulting molecule is a *diastereomer*. Diastereomers are not mirror images, and will have different physical properties. Examples of two diastereomers are (–)-menthone and (–)-isomenthone.

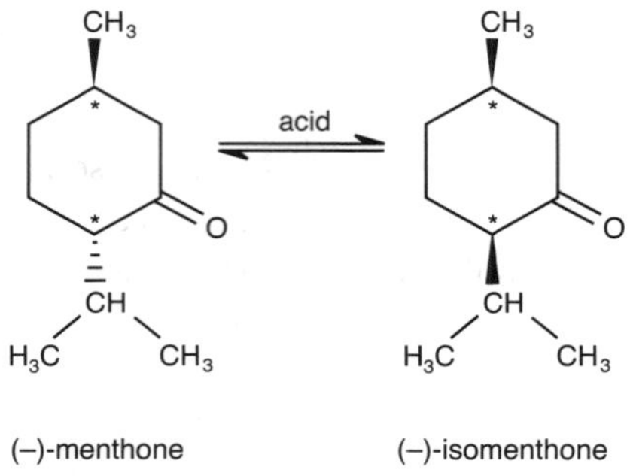

(–)-menthone   (–)-isomenthone

One of the chiral centers of (–)-menthone is next to a carbonyl function, and can be isomerized in acidic conditions. This reaction leads to (–)-isomenthone[2]. Menthone and isomenthone are diastereomers, and therefore they will have different physical properties and they can be separated by gas chromatography (see below). Gas chromatography will be used to determine the extent of isomerization that has taken place in your reaction.

Gas chromatography is a powerful analytical method to analyze volatile products. It is extremely sensitive and can detect trace amounts of material. The eluent in this type of chromatography is a gas, in this case helium, while the stationary phase is a high boiling liquid deposited on a solid substrate. The elution time

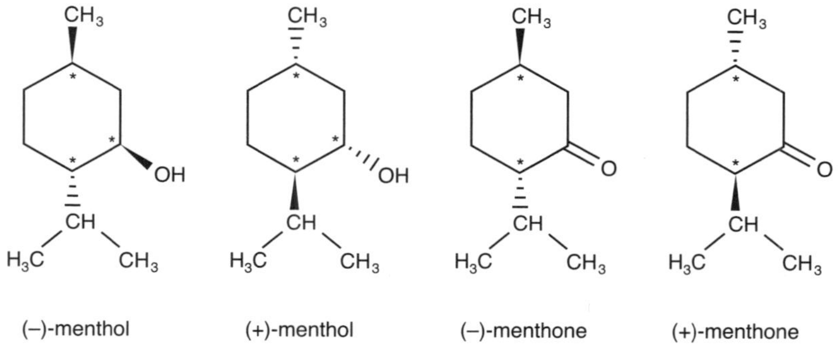

(–)-menthol   (+)-menthol   (–)-menthone   (+)-menthone

of the different components of a mixture will be determined by their boiling points and by the polarity of the compound itself, the polarity of the stationary and the mobile phases. Lower boiling and less polar products will elute first if a moderately polar or very polar stationary phase is used. The eluent is totally nonpolar, so in this case too, as in column chromatography, the stationary phase is more polar than the mobile phase. A detector at the end of the column will determine when compounds (peaks) are eluted from the column. The peaks can be seen using a strip chart recorder, an integrator or a computer.

When gas chromatography is used for analysis, a very small amount of sample is injected (1 μL or less). The gas chromatographic analysis will give us information about the composition and purity of the sample. The sensitivity of the analysis is increased by injecting the minimum amount of sample. A GC can also be used for preparative purposes, and then a much larger amount of sample is injected. The purpose here would be to isolate the different components of a mixture, and collect these different fractions at the gas outlet.

The *isomerization reaction* of menthone to isomenthone involves chemistry which will be covered in lecture during second semester. In essence, a ketone function can be converted to its enol form in acidic (or alkaline) conditions. The enol intermediate has a double bond, which leads to a loss of asymmetry when the carbonyl function is regenerated as shown below for (R)-3-methyl-2-butanone.

Required Reading

- Gas chromatography

- Polarimetry

- Chirality/optical activity chapter in Organic Chemistry textbook.

Aim of the Experiment

- Isomerize menthone to isomenthone.

- Determine the composition of the reaction mixture by GC.

- Solve chirality problem set.

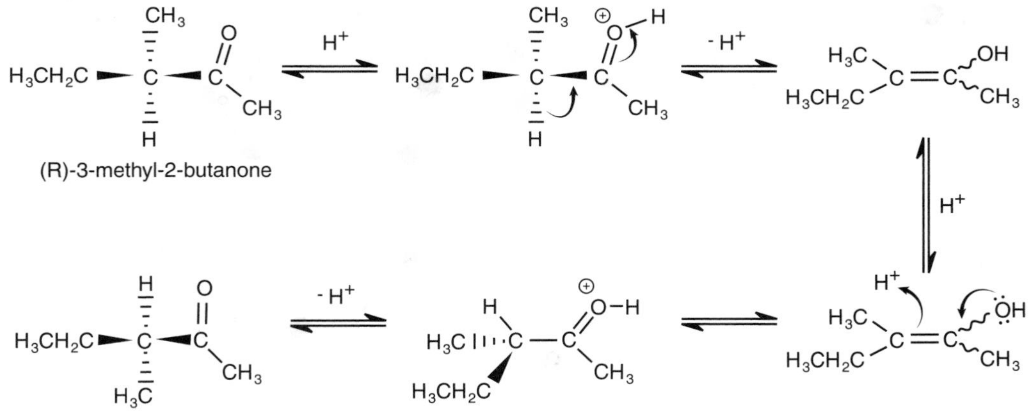

Learning Objectives

• Concept of chirality and molecular asymmetry.

• The relationship between physical constants and enantiomers/diastereomers.

• Use molecular models to reinforce the concept of chirality.

• Learn concept of optional rotation and polarimetry.

Procedure

Mix ~0.25 mL of (–)-menthone with 1.0 mL of glacial acetic acid and 1.0 mL of 1 M HCl in a 10 mL round-bottom flask, and add a boiling chip. Attach a reflux condenser. Heat the mixture to reflux[3] with stirring for 30 minutes, and cool to room temperature.

Work-up

Neutralize the mixture by adding dropwise 4 M NaOH(aq) through the condenser until pH paper indicates neutral. (Leave water running through condenser.) Transfer to a centrifuge tube and extract twice with 3 mL diethyl ether.[4] Dry the combined extracts with anhydrous magnesium sulfate, filter through a plug of cotton in a 5″ pipet into a beaker, and evaporate the ether on top of the hot plate, preferrably in the fume hood. (Make sure the hot plate has cooled down some.)

Analyze the mixture by GC; an example of a GC of a mixture of menthone and isomenthone is shown on page 77. Calculate the percentage of (–)-menthone that isomerized to (–)-isomenthone.[5]

Run an *IR spectrum* of your sample using an IR card.

Notes

1. Amoore, J.E., Johnston, J.W., Jr., Rubin, M. "The Stereochemical Theory of Odor," *Scientific American* **1964**, *210*, 1.

2. The fact that the isomenthone obtained from (–)-menthone is also levorotatory (–), (rotates polarized light to the negative side) is totally coincidental.

3. Reflux means that the mixture is at the boiling temperature of the solvent, in this case mostly water and acetic acid. The temperature is constant, because the temperature of the mixture cannot rise above the temperature of its lowest boiling component. To reflux this mixture, the heating source should be at least at 140 °C; use a heating mantle or other means.

4. Make sure you release the pressure on the centrifuge tube after shaking, because ether has a very low boiling point (35 °C).

5. Consult the section on quantitative analysis using gas chromatography in the Techniques manual.

Discussion

• Explain the underlying logic of the experiment.

• Explain the logic of the work-up procedure.

• Discuss your results.

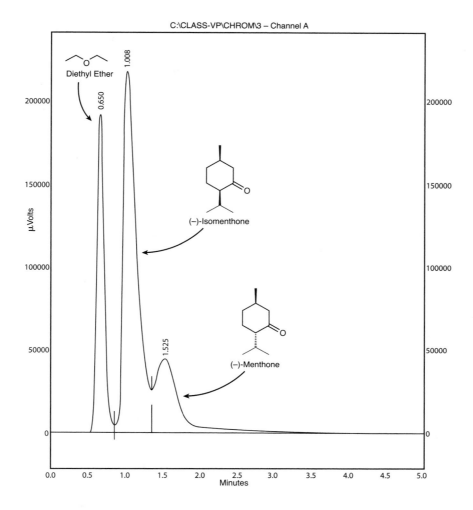

Questions

1. Order the following compounds according to their order of elution of a GC column (from first to last): Ethanol (bp 78.3 °C), acetone (bp 55 °C) and dichloromethane (bp 40 °C).

2. What is an enantiomer?

3. Draw a pair of enantiomers.

4. Give two methods that can distinguish between enantiomers.

5. The following substances are in a mixture:

Compound	mp	bp	Density
acetone	−94	56	0.791
cyclohexene	−104	83	0.811
methanol	−98	65	0.791
ethanol	−130	78	0.785

   If injected into a gas chromatograph, what would be the order of elution?

6. Diagram the components of a gas chromatograph.

7. In gas chromatography the mobile phase is your solvent and the stationary phase is silica gel. True or False?

8. Could you separate a mixture of R- and S- limonene by gas chromatography? Explain.

9. Could you separate a mixture of 1-butene and 2-butene by gas chromatography? Explain.

10. Could you separate a mixture of Z-2-butene and E-2-butene by gas chromatography? Explain.

11. Let's say that you have the D and L enantiomers of the amino acid tryptophan. You are able to run any technique on the compounds available in the lab. What physical properties should be identical, and which should be different if both are solids?

12. Explain the main premise behind the movement of samples through a gas chromatograph. (Discuss the various phases present.)

13. A mixture of pentane (bp 36 °C), neopentane (bp 9.5 °C), and isopentane (bp 28 °C) are analyzed by GC.
    a. Which alkane has the shorter retention time? Why?
    b. Which alkane has the longer retention time? Why?
    c. Explain the effect of the temperature on the retention time, if the column temperature is increased.

Isolation of Limonene from Citrus Fruits

Terpenes are a class of compounds commonly isolated from essential oils of plants, which include a wide variety of fragrances and flavors. They are of great commercial importance in the perfume and flavoring industry, but they are also included in a wide variety of products, such as cleaning products and foods. Menthone and menthol in the previous experiment are examples of terpenes.

Terpenes are composed of two or more five-carbon units based on isoprene (isoprene is 2-methyl-1,3-butadiene). Compounds with two isoprene units, namely 10 carbons, are called monoterpenes, with four isoprene units, i.e., 20 carbons, are diterpenes, etc. Compounds with 15 carbons are called sesquiterpenes (one and a half). Natural rubber is a polymeric terpenoid, in which isoprene is the monomeric unit.

It is important to be able to analyze terpenes and break them up in the isoprene units. These isoprene units have a tail and a head. Any functionality, such as alcohols, ketones, or double bonds, in the terpenoid are ignored while applying the isoprene rule.

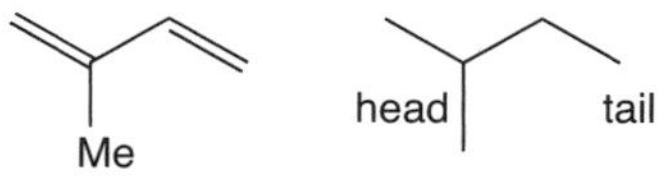

Me

isoprene

head   tail

isoprene unit

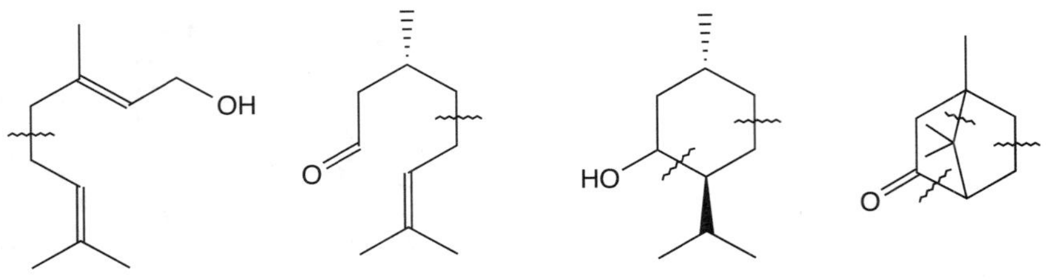

geraniol   citrenellal   menthol   camphor

As can be seen from this very limited selection, terpenes can be found in many natural products. Notice that all of these molecules can be split up into individual isoprene units.

Limonene is a monoterpene oil that is commonly found in citrus fruits, dill, and caraway. It has many industrial applications, from uses in the fragrance and flavor chemistry sectors, to utilization as a solvent, and the manufacture of polymers and adhesives. In addition to these applications, limonene is also the cheapest chiral starting material for organic synthesis.

The R(+)-enantiomer of limonene is commonly isolated from the zest peelings of citrus fruit, while the S(−)-enantiomer is found in pine cones. In a steam distillation, as the water-peel mixture

Bring your own fruit for this lab, preferably two medium-sized oranges, or three medium-sized lemons. The fresher the oranges, the better this experiment will work.

is heated to high temperatures, the limonene will covaporize with water at a much lower temperature than its boiling point, condense, then collect in the receiving flask as a separate layer from the water. The purity of the limonene collected by this method is approximately 95%.

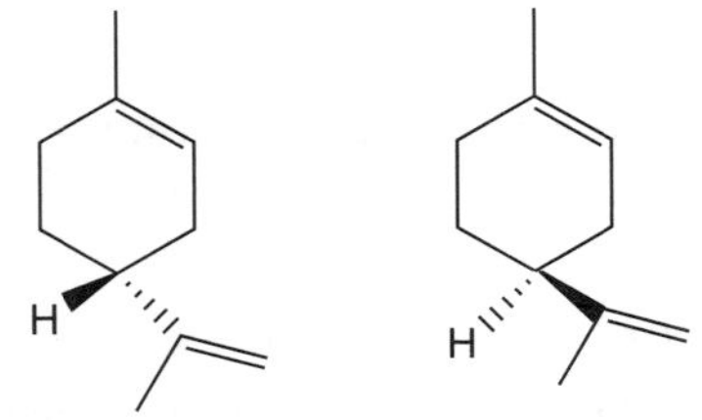

Safety Considerations
Please be cautious when dismantling the distillation apparatus. It is extremely hot!!!

Required Reading
- Steam distillation

- Refractometry

- Gas chromatography

Aim of the Experiment
- Isolate limonene from the peel of a citrus fruit.

- Characterize the isolated limonene.

R(+)-limonene
$\alpha_D^{20} = +123°$

S(-)-limonene
$\alpha_D^{19} = -94°$

Learning Objectives

• Apply steam distillation to a natural mixture.

• Measurement of refractive index.

• Introduction to chirality in natural products.

• Introduction to the structure of terpenes.

Procedure

Set up distillation apparatus with an **empty** fractional distillation column, and a 50 mL graduated cylinder containing 10 mL of saturated aqueous NaCl[1] to serve as the receiving vessel.

Using the fine grating side of a citrus zester, grate the peelings from the fruit[2] into a large beaker. Transfer the gratings with 100 mL of distilled water to a blender, and blend on high speed for a few minutes. Pour the liquid into a 250 mL round-bottom flask, then rinse the blender with an additional 50 mL of water and add to the round-bottom flask. Add two boiling chips.[3] Heat using a heating mantle. Use a high heat setting and continue distilling until only water comes over into the graduated cylinder.

Work-up

Remove the organic layer with a Pasteur pipet and place in a vial.[4] Remove any water from the vial with a pipet. Dry over anhydrous sodium sulfate, and transfer the oil to a small tared vial. Weigh the vial to determine your yield.

To characterize the sample, do the following:
• determine the refractive index (n_D^{20})[5], determine the temperature in the instrument room[6], calculate the % difference between the literature and experimental refractive indices.

• analyze your sample by gas chromatography (inject < 1 μL).

• record an IR spectrum.

• observe the difference in smell for the limonene enantiomers.

Two polarimeters will be set up in the lab, one with (+)-limonene and one with (−)-limonene. The samples are neat.[7] Measure the *optical rotation* α. The optical rotation will depend on the path length in decimeter (1 dm = 0.1 m), therefore the height of the sample has to be measured. Calculate the specific roation [α].

$$[\alpha] = \alpha \,/\, cl$$

where α is the observed rotation in degrees, c is the concentration in g/mL, which in this case would correspond to the density because the samples are neat, and l is the path length in dm.

Notes

1. The NaCl is there again to salt out the organic material. Its presence in the aqueous layer will help the limonene separate from the water layer.

2. Take care when grating the fruit not to remove the white pith layer under the zest peel. Also, watch your fingers!

3. Boiling chips supply an uneven surface to aid the bubble formation in the boiling liquid. Without the boiling chips, the liquid can become overheated, and this might result in uncontrolled bumping.

4. If there is not enough product to pipet out, this separation can be made easier by adding 1–2 mL of diethyl ether. The solvent will then have to be evaporated after the solution has been dried over sodium sulfate.

5. For instructions on how to use the refractometer, consult *Making the Connections*.

6. Be sure to correct the refractive index to 20 °C.

7. No solvent has been added.

Discussion

• Discuss the steam distillation technique, and why it's used rather than other techniques.

• Prove that the compound isolated is what you say it is.

• Discuss chirality in the natural world.

Questions

1. Determine the isoprene units in the following compounds: myrcene, α-pinene, farnesol, β-carotene, and vitamin A. All structures can be found in your Organic Chemistry textbook.

2. Catalytic hydrogenation of R-limonene leads to two isomers. Which ones?

3. How would you be able to tell from the IR spectrum if your limonene is not completely dry?

4. The refractive index of a compound is measured to be 1.3780 at 27 °C. Correct the refractive index to 20 °C.

5. What is the molar concentration of a 1 L solution of 35 ml of limonene (d = 0.84) in hexane?

6. You collected 2.4 g of zest from the oranges you brought in. After steam distillation, you obtained 350 mg of limonene. What is your % yield?

11a

Alkenes by Elimination

Two main pathways exist to prepare alkenes by elimination reactions. Both dehydration of an alcohol (loss of H_2O) and dehydrohalogenation of an alkyl halide (loss of HX) will lead to unsaturated products. Dehydration of an alcohol occurs in highly acidic medium, while strongly alkaline conditions are necessary for the dehydrohalogenation of an alkyl halide. The direction of elimination will be governed by Zaitsev's rule, which states that the most highly substituted alkene will be formed preferentially.

Even though at first sight these two reactions might seem rather similar, they proceed by completely different mechanisms. As is seen in the reaction scheme below, in the dehydration of an alcohol, the first step is the protonation of the OH substituent, resulting in the conversion of a poor leaving group, OH^-, into a very good leaving group, H_2O. The protonated alcohol can undergo elimination by either an E_1 (first order) or an E_2 (second order) mechanism. In an E_1 mechanism, a monomolecular elimination of water will result in an alkyl cation, which then eliminates a proton. On the other hand, in the E_2 mechanism, a bimolecular reaction occurs in which water acts as a base, abstracting a β–hydrogen. Both reactions lead to formation of an alkene. Similarly, the dehydrohalogenation can also occur either by an E_1 or an E_2 mechanism. The reaction conditions used in today's experiment, namely strong base, favor the bimolecular reaction. The base abstracts a β-hydrogen,

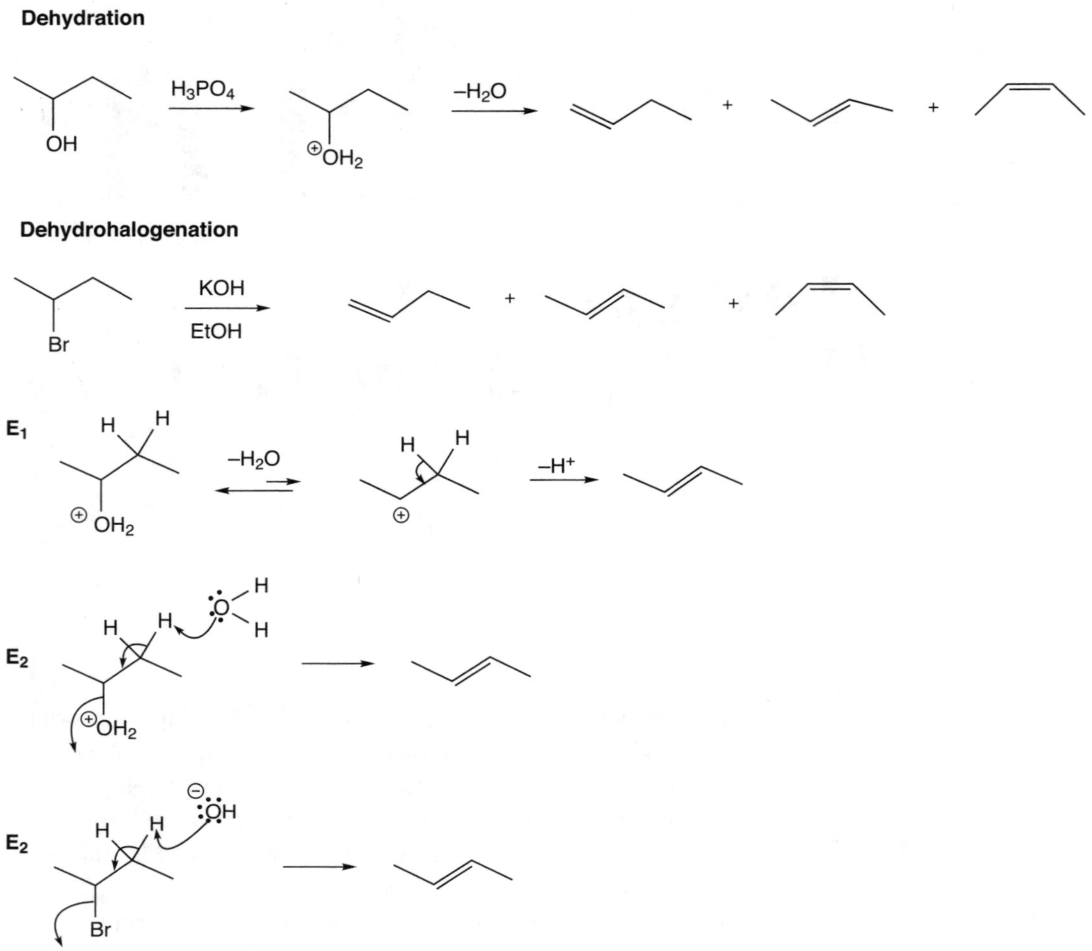

Dehydration

Dehydrogenation

E$_1$

E$_2$

E$_2$

a double bond is formed and Br⁻ is eliminated from the substrate, all in one concerted reaction step. The different mechanisms will result in different proportions of the butenes. Don't forget to take into account that 1-butene can also be formed.

Required Reading
(All in your organic chemistry textbook)

- Dehydrohalogenation of RX

- Dehydration of ROH

- Detailed mechanism of elimination

Aim of the Experiment

- Run the base-catalyzed dehydrohalogenation of 2-bromobutane and the acid-catalyzed dehydration of 2-butanol to obtain a mixture of butenes.

- Analyze the gaseous products by gas chromatography.

Learning Objectives

- Learn about the elimination mechanisms, E1 and E2.

- Learn how to collect gaseous products.

- Apply gas chromatography to the analysis of gaseous products.

Procedure

Collect a syringe needle, flexible tubing, and a septum-capped glass tube from the preproom.

Safety Considerations

Use gloves when handling the concentrated acids and the concentrated alkaline solution. In case of an accidental spill on your hands, wash thoroughly with lots and lots of water for a minimum of 15 minutes.

Butenes are flammable gases; no flames are allowed in the lab.

©Hayden-McNeil, LLC

The setup used for both procedures is designed to collect the gaseous products of these reactions. A 10 mL round-bottom flask with a magnetic stirrer is equipped with the thermometer adapter. Don't forget the O-rings, as this setup has to be gas-tight. A Pasteur pipet is inverted in the thermometer adapter (it is the same size as a thermometer, so it fits tightly). A piece of thin tygon tubing is connected to the Pasteur pipet tip. A piece of glass tubing has a septum on one end. It is filled with water and inverted in a beaker filled with water. A test tube filled with water is also placed upside down in the beaker. The test tube should be calibrated: place a mark at the 8 mL level. The end of the tygon tubing is inserted in the bottom of first the test tube.

At the beginning of the reaction, the gases are collected in a test tube, and later on in the glass tube capped with a septum. The reaction product will displace the water in the tubes.

Dehydration of 2-Butanol

2-Butanol (0.4 mL) is placed in the 10 mL RB flask and 0.6 mL of a mixture of concentrated phosphoric acid H_3PO_4 and concentrated sulfuric acid H_2SO_4 is added. After the mixture is well mixed, the flask is connected to the tubing. Place the reaction flask in a water bath and heat to boiling. The first 10–15 mL of gas[1] are collected in the test tube, and then the tubing is moved to the septum-capped tube. Continue heating until you collect about 7–8 mL of the gaseous reaction product.

Remove the tubing from the water bath **before** removing the flask from the heating mantle or **before** turning down the heat.[2] Make sure you securely fasten the tube containing your reaction product in the water bath, so it doesn't topple over.

Collect about 500 µL (or 1 mL) from the product mixture by inserting an air-tight syringe through the septum, and analyze by gas chromatography. The order of elution of the products will be as follows: 1-butene, *trans*-2-butene and *cis*–2-butene.

Dehydrohalogenation of 2-Bromobutane

In a 10 mL round-bottom flask, mix 3.0 mL of a 30% KOH solution in absolute ethanol with 0.3 mL of 2-bromobutane. After the mixture is well mixed, the flask is connected to the tubing. Place the reaction flask in a water bath and increase the heat to boiling. The first 10–15 mL of gas[1] are collected in the test tube, and then the tubing is moved to the septum-capped tube. Continue heating until you collect about 7–8 mL of the gaseous reaction product.

Remove the tubing from the water bath **before** removing the flask from the heating mantle or **before** turning down the heat.[2] Make sure you securely fasten the tube containing your reaction product in the water bath, so it doesn't topple over.

Collect about 500 µL (or 1 mL) from the product mixture by inserting an air-tight syringe through the septum and analyze by gas chromatography. The order of elution of the products will be as follows: 1-butene, *trans*-2-butene, and *cis*-2-butene.

Notes

1. The first 8 mL are mostly air.

2. If the tubing is not removed from the water bath before cooling the reaction flask, water will be sucked into the reaction vessel, which contains concentrated acids. This is obviously not a good thing to do!

Discussion

• Calculate the relative yields of the different butenes formed using the triangulation method on the gas chromatogram.

• Discuss the relative product distribution in relationship to the different mechanisms and Zaitsev's rule.

• Compare the results of the acidic dehydration with the alkaline dehydrohalogenation. Compare the amounts of *trans*-2-butene and *cis*-2-butene, and the total amount of 2-butene with 1-butene.

• Discuss if the reactions were regioselective.

Questions

1. What is Zaitsev's rule?

2. Give the mechanism for the acid-catalyzed E1 reaction of 2-butanol.

3. Give the mechanism for the base-catalyzed E2 reaction of 2-bromobutane. Draw all possible products.

4. You expect three products from the elimination reaction performed in class. Most of the class gets three peaks on their gas chromatographs; you get only two. How do you determine which two of the three products you have?

5. The E2 mechanism is a one-step mechanism. True or False?

6. Which of these two alcohols would you expect to be more reactive under H_3PO_4/aq conditions? Why? Give the structure of the main product in both cases.
1-phenyl-1-propanol and 1-cyclohexyl-1-propanol

7. In your elimination reaction experiment which of the three compounds represents the highest peak observed in your chromatogram: 1-butene, (E)–2-butene or (Z)-2-butene. Why?

8. Give the structures for the alkenes produced by the dehydration of 2,3-dimethyl-2-butanol with conc. H_2SO_4. Circle the major product.

9. You are given a bottle of concentrated sulfuric acid (13 M). However, you need 1 M sulfuric acid, and nobody is present in the preproom to make it for you. How would you make 200 mL of the 1 M aqueous solution?

10. You perform the reaction of 2 mL pinacolyl alcohol (3,3-dimethyl-2-butanol, d = 0.812) with 5 mL of a mixture of concentrated phosphoric acid and concentrated sulfuric acid. You collect the product, and obtain 0.85 g. What is the product? Calculate the % yield.

S$_N$1 and S$_N$2 Reactions

Due to the difference in electronegativity between carbon and halogen, with the halogen being a lot more electronegative, a polarization exists in a carbon-halogen bond. The carbon atom acquires a partial positive charge and the halogen a partial negative charge. The carbon takes on electrophilic character, meaning electron-loving, while the halogen will be nucleophilic, meaning nucleus-loving.

Nucleophilic substitution of an alkyl halide consists of the substitution of the halogen (leaving group) with a nucleophile. The attacking nucleophile can be either a neutral species or an anion. The original halogen in the reacting molecule will be pushed out by the entering nucleophile, and its anion, X$^-$, will be the leaving group.

$$\text{Nu:}^- \;+\; \overset{\delta+}{R}\!\!-\!\!\overset{\delta-}{X} \longrightarrow R\!-\!Nu \;+\; X^-$$

$$\text{Nu:} \;+\; \overset{\delta+}{R}\!\!-\!\!\overset{\delta-}{X} \longrightarrow [R\!-\!Nu]^+ \;+\; X^-$$

As you have learned in lecture, two possible mechanisms exist for the nucleophilic substitution reaction, namely a stepwise mechanism or a one-step concerted mechanism. The stepwise mechanism proceeds via a cationic intermediate and follows first-order reaction kinetics, therefore the name S$_N$1. The one-step concerted mechanism does not involve an intermediate and follows second-order reaction kinetics because two molecules are involved in the rate-determining step. Therefore,

S$_N$1

$$R-X \xrightleftharpoons[EtOH]{} R^+ X^- \xrightarrow[EtOH]{AgNO_3} R-OEt + AgX\downarrow + HNO_3$$

S$_N$2

$$R-X \xrightarrow[acetone]{NaI} R-I + NaX\downarrow$$

X = Cl or Br

this reaction is named S$_N$2. The stability of the intermediate alkyl cation and the polarity of the solvent will play a big role in the rate of a S$_N$1 reaction, while the steric hindrance around the reacting center will be of prime importance in the S$_N$2 reaction. The mechanism is determined by several factors, such as the structure of the alkyl halide, the leaving group ability of the halogen, the nucleophilicity of the incoming nucleophile, and the polarity of the medium.

It is within the range of possibilities to force a nucleophilic substitution to proceed through either the S$_N$1 or the S$_N$2 mechanism by manipulating the reaction conditions. A reaction on an alkyl halide can be compelled to proceed through the S$_N$1 mechanism by using silver nitrate (AgNO$_3$) in ethanol. The nitrate anion is non-nucleophilic and ethanol is a very polar solvent, which helps to stabilize the intermediate alkyl cation. The oxygen of ethanol is the most nucleophilic species in this reaction, resulting in formation of an ethyl ether derivative. On the other hand, using sodium iodide in acetone greatly favors the S$_N$2 mechanism. Iodide is an excellent nucleophile, favoring the bimolecular reaction, and acetone is only a moderately polar solvent, which discourages the formation of an intermediate alkyl cation.

Notice that in both reactions a precipitate is formed, silver chloride or bromide in the S$_N$1 reaction and sodium chloride or bromide in the

S$_N$2 reaction. The precipitation of a product from a reaction solution will drive the equilibrium toward the right, according to Le Châtelier's Principle. The formation of precipitate is very fortunate (but obviously planned) in this reaction, because not only will it drive the reaction in the desired direction, but it will give a visual clue to determine if the reaction is proceeding and how fast.

Required Reading
*   Nucleophilic substitution in your Organic Chemistry textbook.

Aim of the Experiment
*   Compare the different mechanisms of nucleophilic substitution reactions.

*   Study the effect of substrate structure.

Learning Objectives
*   Become familiar with the different aspects of the nucleophilic substitution reactions.

*   Be able to predict the reactivity of different reaction mixtures; i.e., different substrates with different reaction conditions.

Before the Lab
Study the structures of all the alkyl halides that you will be using in this lab. Based on your knowledge of the S$_N$1 and S$_N$2 reactions, predict the reactivity of each of these alkyl halides.

Procedure

Two reagents are available for these substitution reactions, namely AgNO$_3$ in ethanol (S$_N$1) and NaI in acetone (S$_N$2). You will run the reaction of each of the alkyl halides with these two reagents and observe the reaction rates. Reactive alkyl halides will react within a few minutes at room temperature. For moderately reactive halides, some heating will be necessary to achieve reaction, i.e., a precipitate, while unreactive halides will not produce any precipitate.

Label nine test tubes for use with the different alkyl halides. Place 4 drops (~0.2 mL) of each of the alkyl halides in the different test tubes.

Preheat a water bath to 50 °C.[1] Add 2 mL of a 15 % NaI in acetone solution to each test tube and shake the content to mix. Note the time of mixing. Observe the test tubes and note the time necessary for a precipitate to form. Wait about 5–10 minutes. Place the test tubes with no precipitate in the water bath at 50 °C for 5 minutes. Cool the test tubes to room temperature and note whether a precipitate has formed or not. Record all your observations in your notebook.

Raise the temperature of the water bath to about 80 °C[2] for the next set of reactions.

Repeat the same procedure with the series of alkyl halides with 2 mL of a 1 % silver nitrate in ethanol solution. Again record all observations at room temperature, and heat the samples that do not react at room temperature in the water bath for about 5 minutes.

From your observations you will be able to determine the reactivities of these different alkyl halides in both S$_N$1 and S$_N$2 conditions, and draw your own conclusions.

Notes

1. The boiling point of the first solvent used, acetone, is 55 °C. Therefore a water bath temperature higher than 50 °C would result in loss of solvent.

2. The boiling point of ethanol is 78 °C.

Discussion

- Compare the relative reactivities of the alkyl halide substrates used in this experiment to both S$_N$1 and S$_N$2 reaction conditions.

Questions

1. You wish to substitute the bromine in the following molecules with a nucleophile. Explain whether the given molecule would react by the S$_N$1 or S$_N$2 mechanism and explain why. 1-methyl-1-bromo-cyclohexane, 1-bromopropane, 2-bromohexane.

2. Why does benzyl bromide react under both S$_N$1 conditions and S$_N$2 conditions?

3. Why is bromobenzene nonreactive under both S$_N$1 and S$_N$2 conditions?

4. Given the following structures that react by S$_N$1, which would react fastest and which would react slowest? Give your reasoning. 5-bromo-1,3-pentadiene, bromocyclopentane,(R)-2-bromo-2-methylhexane.

5. If bromocyclohexane reacts faster than chlorocyclohexane in an S$_N$2 reaction, what could be the reason?

6. Tertiary-butyl iodide reacts faster than *t*-butyl bromide via S$_N$2 mechanism because iodide is a better leaving group than bromide. True or False?

7. 1-Chlorobutane (2.5 mL, d = 0.886) in 20 mL of acetone is reacted with 90 mL of a 15 wt% solution of NaI in acetone. After work-up, you obtain 1.3 g of 1-iodobutane. Which is the limiting reagent? What is your % yield?

8. Your TA tells you to make 200 mL of a 1 wt% AgNO$_3$ solution in ethanol, because the stockroom just ran out of the stuff. How would you do this?

9. To promote the S$_N$1 mechanism we used AgNO$_3$ in a polar, protic solvent. True or False? Why?

10. The rate of reaction for the S$_N$2 mechanism is dependent on the concentration of both nucleophile and the electrophile. True or False? Justify your answer.

11. Account for the rapid rate of ethanolysis of ClCH$_2$OCH$_2$CH$_3$ even though the substrate is a primary halide. Hint: The reaction of the substrate with ethanol proceeds by S$_N$1 mechanism. Draw the Lewis structures.

1b

Nuclear Magnetic Resonance Spectroscopy: A Second Visit

NMR Spectroscopy is a frequently used spectroscopic method used in organic chemistry. It is, however, a complex technique, and it is not easy.

As you will be exposed to NMR quite a few times this semester, a refresher problem set has been designed to help you. Please review the NMR introduction in Experiment 8a and also the NMR chapter in your organic chemistry textbook and in *Making the Connections*.

2b

Diels-Alder Reaction

The Diels-Alder reaction is a [4 + 2] concerted cycloaddition and one of the most important reactions in organic chemistry. The reaction was first investigated by Otto Diels and Kurt Alder in Germany, and they reported their findings in 1928.[1] Over the years they reported on a large variety of dienes which would react with olefins to form cyclic compounds in a very specific manner. This reaction builds rings very efficiently and easily, and is stereospecific.

The Diels-Alder reaction is classified as a *pericyclic* reaction, that is a reaction that involves a cyclic rearrangement of bonding electrons, meaning that the bonds are broken and formed simultaneously. Therefore this reaction takes place in a single step, without intermediates. This explains why the reaction is stereospecific, because the substituents are never given a chance to "switch around."

It was not until Woodward and Hoffmann published their treatise on the "Conservation of Orbital Symmetry" in the early 1960s that the mechanism of the Diels-Alder reaction was completely explained on the basis of molecular orbitals and the retention of symmetry.[2] It stated that a [4 + 2] concerted reaction was thermally *allowed*, meaning that a concerted (simultaneous) cyclic reaction involving 4 electrons of one reactant and 2 electrons of the other reactant was possible. In contrast, a concerted [2 + 2] cycloaddition is thermally *forbidden*, meaning that the cycloaddition of two olefins to form a cyclobutane cannot proceed via a concerted reaction, but has to involve an intermediate.

The Diels-Alder reaction is an industrially very important reaction in the synthesis of insecticides and pharmaceuticals. It is a very efficient reaction, as both reagents are completely incorporated in the product.

Required Reading
• Diels-Alder reaction, Organic textbook.

Aim of the Experiment
• Perform a Diels-Alder cycloaddition.

• Hydrolyze the intermediate product.

Learning Objectives
• Run two consecutive reactions.

• Learn how to work with a low boiling liquid.

• Experience the use of greener solvents.

• Learn different work-up procedures based on solubility.

Comment on Lab Procedures for Second Semester Organic Chemistry Lab
As a student you might find the style in which the lab procedures for second semester are written somewhat disconcerting and terse. These procedures are written in the style used in publications in the literature. They do not have any great detail, but they do provide you with all the necessary information needed to run the experiment. You will have to rely on your knowledge of the techniques you learned in first semester lab. Additional information is also provided in the Notes.

Procedure
In an effort to make some of these experiments more "green," we have replaced the classical organic solvent toluene with polyethylene glycol (PEG 200).

Weigh out an amount of maleic anhydride between 180 and 200 mg and place it along with a magnetic stirrer in a 10 mL round-bottom flask.[3] Equip the round-bottom flask with a water condenser and add 1 mL PEG 200 (polyethylene glycol MW 200). Calculate how much 2,3-dimethyl-1,3-butadiene ($d = 0.72$ g/mL) should be added to achieve equimolar conditions. Use a 1 mL syringe to add 2,3-dimethylbutadiene to the flask and heat the reaction mixture slowly to 60–70 °C for about 30 minutes.[4]

Work-up[5]
Pour the reaction mixture into a beaker containing ~50 mL water. The cycloaddition product will precipitate out.[6] Determine the melting point (lit.[7] m.p. 78–79 °C) and yield. Record the IR spectrum of the anhydride.

To hydrolyze the cyclic anhydride to the diacid, mix the crystals with approximately 10 mL of water in a small beaker and add 2–3 drops aqueous HCl as catalyst. Heat until all the solid dissolves.[8] This should take less than 15 minutes.

Work-up
Cool the aqueous solution and collect the crystals. Determine the melting point (lit.[7] 204 °C) and yield, and record the IR spectrum using the IR cards.[9]

Notes

1. Diels, O., Alder, K. *Ann. Chem.* **1928,** *460,* 98.

2. Hoffmann, R., Woodward, R.B. *J. Amer. Chem. Soc.,* **1965,** 87, 2046, 4388.

3. Record the exact weight of maleic anhydride. You need this to calculate the needed amount of 2,3 dimethyl-1,3-butadiene.

4. The temperature has to be controlled due to the low boiling point of 2,3 dimethyl-1,3-butadiene. Heat it up slowly at the onset.

5. After the reaction is complete, the product has to be isolated using a work-up procedure.

6. The anhydride crystallizes as white needle-like crystals. It is named 4,5-dimethyl-cyclohexene-1,2-dicarboxylic acid anhydride.

7. Boeseken, J.; De Rijck van der Gracht, W.J.F. *Rec. Trav. Chim. Pays-Bas* **1937,** *56,* 1203.

8. The anhydride melts in the reaction mixture because its melting point is lower than the boiling point of water. It forms oil drops on the bottom of the beaker. Make sure these "oil drops" have disappeared before stopping the reaction. The crystals forming in the boiling water are the diacid precipitating out.

9. The dicarboxylic acid derivative is very insoluble and has a great tendency to crystallize. If you have trouble getting a good sample for IR using dichloromethane, try acetone. This reaction product seems to have less of a tendency to crystallize from acetone.

■ Discussion

- Describe mechanism of cycloaddition.

- Discuss reaction conditions.

- Discuss mechanism of hydrolysis. (Why is acid added?)

- Discuss work-up procedures. What's the logic behind the procedure?

- Discuss the two infrared spectra.

IR spectrum of 4,5-dimethyl-cyclohexene-1,2-dicarboxylic acid

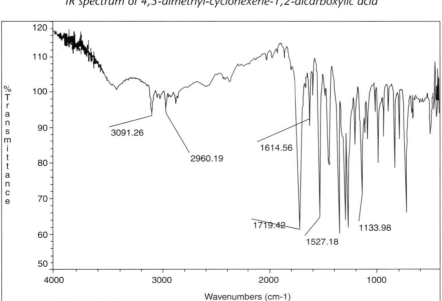

Questions

1. Which side reaction could occur in this experiment if the toluene were not completely dry? Show reaction.

2. Draw the exo and endo product for the reaction of cyclopentadiene and maleic anhydride. Which one will be favored?

3. Assuming we start with 200 mg of cyclopentadiene and 300 mg of maleic anhydride, and 375 mg of the cycloadduct anhydride is obtained:
   which is the limiting reagent?
   calculate the percent yield for the anhydride.

4. If the hydrolysis to the diacid is not complete, how could you separate the desired diacid from the unhydrolyzed anhydride by extraction?

5. Complete the following reactions. Indicate the stereochemistry when appropriate.

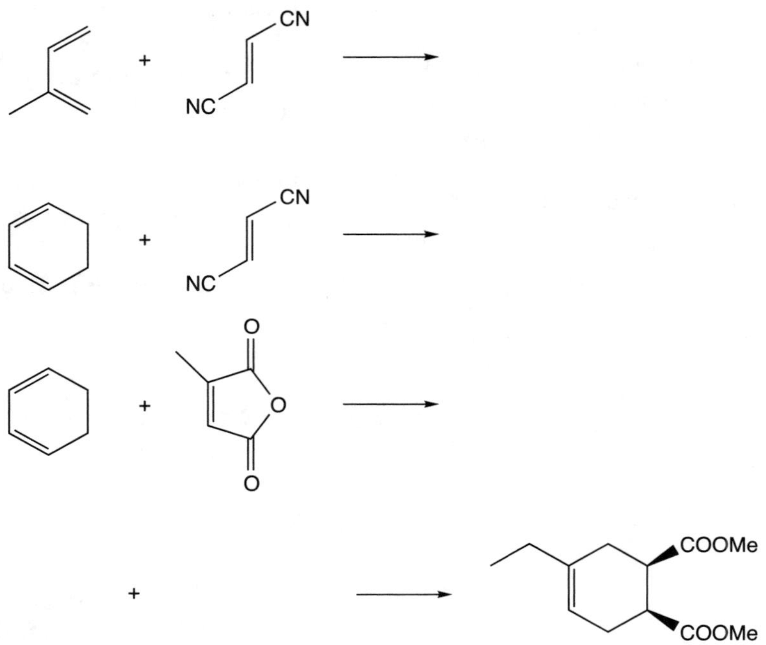

3b

Nitration of Methyl Benzoate, a Macroscale Synthesis

In electrophilic aromatic substitution, a hydrogen on the aromatic ring is replaced by an electrophilic reagent. In the present experiment, methyl benzoate is reacted with nitric acid to form methyl *m*-nitrobenzoate.

Aromatic compounds are surrounded by their π-electron clouds, which make them very unreactive to nucleophiles. Electrophiles are better suited for reaction with an aromatic ring. However highly reactive electrophilic reagents are needed, because any reaction to the aromatic ring results in the loss of the resonance stabilization. The nitronium ion is an example of a highly reactive electrophilic reagent. The nitronium ion NO_2^+ is formed in a mixture of nitric acid and concentrated sulfuric acid. Nitric acid acts as a base in this equilibrium as shown below.

The nitronium ion is reactive enough to react with benzene to form nitrobenzene. As a matter of fact, it is so reactive that the reaction of toluene with a mixture of nitric and sulfuric acid can result in the formation of 2,4,6-trinitrotoluene (TNT)[1] in spite of the deactivating character of the nitro groups. In this experiment we will use methyl benzoate as the substrate because the methyl ester group is a deactivating group, thereby making this experiment quite a bit safer.

The methyl ester group is a meta-director, and the main product in this reaction is methyl *m*-nitrobenzoate.[2] You can find the detailed mechanism of the nitration of an aromatic compound in your Organic Chemistry textbook.

This reaction will be run on a macroscale. Most of the experiments run in this laboratory course are run on a microscale. The microscale has many advantages, such as increased safety, sturdier glassware, and most importantly, a great reduction in chemical waste. However, most organic reactions in a synthetic environment are run on a larger scale. This experiment is designed to give you an idea of the scale at which reactions are normally performed.

Required Reading
- Electrophilic aromatic substitution in Organic Chemistry textbook.

Aim of the Experiment
- Perform an electrophilic aromatic substitution.

- Perform a reaction on a macroscale.

Learning Objectives
- Experience a reaction on a macroscale.

- Run a reaction with concentrated acids.

- Understand the link between reaction temperature and control of reaction path.

- Identify and determine purity of the product based on spectroscopic methods.

Procedure
Important: The temperature of the reaction mixture should be kept at or below 15 °C to avoid excessive formation of byproduct.

Safety Considerations
Nitric acid and sulfuric acid are both very strong acids, and therefore corrosive. The mixture of the two is even more corrosive. Wear gloves. Any acid spill on the skin should be washed off very thoroughly.

Place 12 mL of concentrated sulfuric acid in a 150 mL beaker and cool to about 0 °C using an ice-water bath. Add about 6 g of methyl benzoate using a volumetric cylinder,[3] and cool again to 0 °C. VERY SLOWLY add a cooled to 0 °C mixture of 4 mL of nitric acid and 4 mL of sulfuric acid using a Pasteur pipet. Stir continuously with a plastic spatula and keep the temperature below 15 °C.[4]

Work-up

Allow the mixture to warm to room temperature and wait 15 minutes. Pour the reaction mixture onto about 50 g of crushed ice[5] in a larger beaker. Stir and when all ice has melted, filter the mixture. Wash the solids on the filter twice with 25 mL of cold water, and then twice with 10 mL of cold methanol. Weigh the crude product and recrystallize from methanol.[6] Filter and dry the crystals on top of the Hirsch funnel.

Determine the yield. Determine the melting point (lit. 78 °C) and record the IR spectrum using the IR card. Submit your sample for NMR;[7] $CDCl_3$ will be used as solvent and TMS (tetramethylsilane) as standard.

Notes

1. Methyl is an activating group and ortho-para director.

2. Possible side reactions include dinitrated product, as well as ortho- or para-substituted compounds.

3. Don't weigh the methyl benzoate. Instead calculate the volume necessary using the density of methyl benzoate.

4. The temperature will control how fast you can add the sulfuric/nitric acid mixture. Use an alcohol thermometer to monitor the reaction temperature.

5. Don't weigh the ice, the quantity of ice is not very important. There should be enough ice so that not all of it has melted when the last drops of the reaction mixture are added.

6. A minimal amount of methanol should be used.

7. It is extremely important that your sample be dry when you submit it for NMR. Place 15–20 mg of sample (~ 2–3 small crystals) in the NMR tube, and show it to your TA. He/she will add the necessary amount of $CDCl_3$ to your sample before submitting it for analysis.

Discussion

• Explain electrophilic aromatic substitution mechanism.

• Discuss the electrophile.

• Discuss the choice of methyl benzoate.

• Discuss the logic of the work-up procedure.

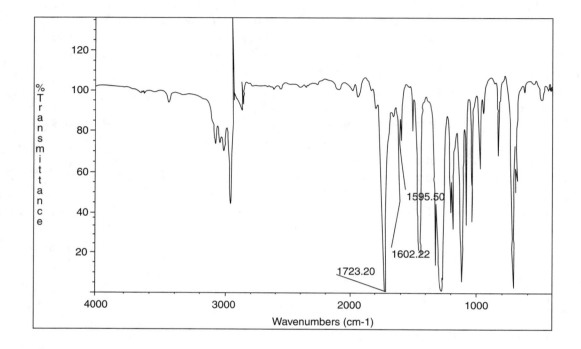

IR spectrum of methyl benzoate
(Note the sharp peaks due to the polyethylene film around 2950 cm⁻¹)

NMR SPECTRA

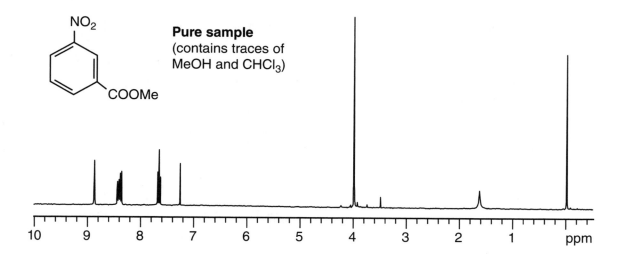

Pure sample
(contains traces of MeOH and CHCl₃)

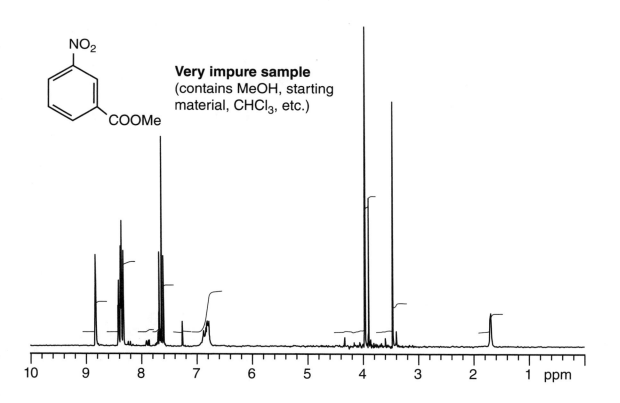

Very impure sample
(contains MeOH, starting material, CHCl₃, etc.)

Questions

1. Write the chemical reaction showing how the electrophile for the nitration of methyl benzoate was formed.

2. Why does methyl benzoate, which is water insoluble, dissolve in concentrated H_2SO_4?

3. In the nitration of methyl benzoate, yields of product were moderate at best. Which undesired products may have formed which would have lowered the yield? What procedural error may have led to these products?

4. The nitro substituent was introduced in the meta position of the methyl benzoate. Why does it preferentially occur at meta, other than para or ortho? Show structures to prove your reasoning. (Be aware that it *preferentially* goes to meta, which means that the other reactions are not totally excluded.)

5. Calculate the percent yield and percent recovery for today's reaction. (Hint: To determine if the acids are limiting reagent, you must know the concentration of the acids.)

6. Label the IR spectra in the book and the IR and NMR spectra obtained in lab. Does the final spectrum indicate product? Why? Identify any impurities in spectra and suggest methods for removing these impurities. Can you tell if your product is dinitrated from the IR?

7. During the procedure, several washes with cold methanol were done. Why was it important to use cold methanol?

8. Why was it important to use a minimum amount of methanol for recrystallization?

9. What removes the hydrogen from the sp^3 carbon in the cationic reaction intermediate to allow the aromatic ring to reform?

4b

Oxidation of Borneol to Camphor

The oxidation of alcohols leads to aldehydes and carboxylic acids, or to ketones, depending on the structure of the alcohol substrate. The first question would be how oxidation and reduction are defined in organic chemistry.

In general chemistry, oxidation is defined as a loss of electrons, while in a reduction electrons are gained. Iron, for example, is oxidized by the atmosphere to its oxide. Fe^0 is oxidized up to Fe^{3+} with the loss of 3 electrons, forming Fe_2O_3. Most organic compounds, though, have no charges, which makes it a little bit more difficult to recognize oxidations and reductions. An oxidation is usually thought of as an addition of oxygen (or halogens) or as a loss of hydrogen, while in a reduction hydrogens are added to the substrate. More specifically, in the oxidation of an alcohol, for example, C–H bonds are being replaced by C–O bonds. In the scheme below, the symbol [O] indicates any oxidizing agent. Primary alcohols can be oxidized to an aldehyde, which in turn can be oxidized very easily to the corresponding carboxylic acid, while a secondary alcohol oxidation leads to the corresponding ketone.

Another method of distinguishing oxidations and reductions in organic chemistry is by calculating the oxidation number of carbon in the different molecules. Hydrogen in an organic molecule would correspond to a 1+ charge, while oxygen O corresponds to 2–. Halogens

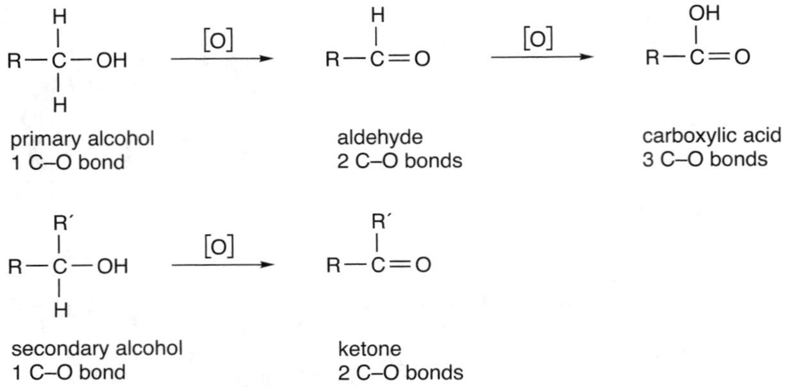

primary alcohol
1 C–O bond

aldehyde
2 C–O bonds

carboxylic acid
3 C–O bonds

secondary alcohol
1 C–O bond

ketone
2 C–O bonds

correspond to 1–, also based on their position in the periodic table. Carbon substituents on the carbon atom in question are being ignored. Armed with these few facts, we can calculate the oxidation number of carbon in the alcohols and their oxidation products. In the schemes shown we can clearly see that an oxidation in organic chemistry always involves the loss of an even number of electrons at a time; for example the primary alcohol C is oxidized from 1– to 1+ in the aldehyde, and to 3+ in the carboxylic acid. The highest possible oxidation state for carbon is 4+ in carbon dioxide CO_2 and in the unstable carbonic acid HO–CO–OH, while the lowest oxidation state is 4– in methane CH_4.

Many of the oxidizing agents in organic chemistry are based on Cr. Chromic acid H_2CrO_4 is a commonly used oxidant and is prepared by dissolving sodium dichromate in a mixture of sulfuric acid and water. The same active species is obtained by adding chromium trioxide CrO_3 to dilute sulfuric acid. The Cr has oxidation state 6+ in these oxidants. Milder oxidants can be obtained by mixing CrO_3 with pyridine to form PCC, which allows you to obtain the aldehyde from the corresponding primary alcohol. Other oxidants include sodium hypochlorite (bleach, NaOCl), halogens, or enzymes.

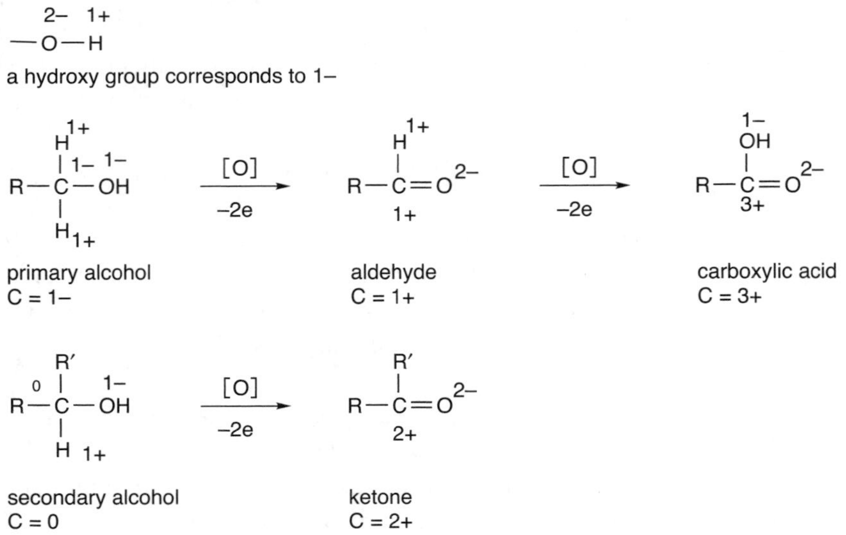

a hydroxy group corresponds to 1–

primary alcohol
C = 1–

aldehyde
C = 1+

carboxylic acid
C = 3+

secondary alcohol
C = 0

ketone
C = 2+

$$Na_2Cr_2O_7 \;+\; H_2O \;+\; 2H_2SO_4 \;\longrightarrow\; 2\,HO-\overset{\overset{\displaystyle O}{\|}}{\underset{\underset{\displaystyle O}{\|}}{Cr}}-OH \;+\; 2Na^+ \;+\; 2HSO_4^-$$

sodium
dichromate

chromic acid

$$CrO_3 \;+\; H_2O \;\underset{\substack{dilute \\ H_2SO_4}}{\longrightarrow}\; HO-\overset{\overset{\displaystyle O}{\|}}{\underset{\underset{\displaystyle O}{\|}}{Cr}}-OH \;\rightleftharpoons\; H^+ \;+\; {}^-O-\overset{\overset{\displaystyle O}{\|}}{\underset{\underset{\displaystyle O}{\|}}{Cr}}-OH$$

chromium
trioxide

chromic acid

acid chromate
ion

In this experiment we will oxidize a secondary alcohol, borneol, to the corresponding ketone, camphor. The mechanism of this oxidation probably involves the intermediacy of the chromate ester of the alcohol. Elimination of the chromate ester under the influence of water gives the ketone. The Cr^{6+} species is reduced to a Cr^{4+} species. Both sodium dichromate and chromic acid are orange in color, while the reduced species are green to greenish blue. The color change allows us to follow the progress of the reaction. In fact, this color change can be used as a test for the presence of an oxidizable alcohol.[1]

In this experiment we will follow the progress of the reaction by a more sophisticated method, namely by TLC (thin-layer chromatography). During the first semester of organic lab, you used TLC for analytical purposes, to determine the composition of a mixture obtained from natural products such as spinach. However, TLC is also a very convenient and fast method to follow the progress of a reaction. At the beginning of the reaction the starting materials will show up as spots on the TLC plate, and as the reaction progresses the product will display a spot. The reaction will be finished when the starting material can no longer be detected. Even though both starting material (borneol) and product (camphor) in this reaction are colorless and not UV-active, we can visualize the spots using staining reagents.

Required Reading

- Oxidation of alcohols

- TLC

$$R-\overset{\overset{\displaystyle R'}{|}}{\underset{\underset{\displaystyle H}{|}}{C}}-OH \;+\; HO-\overset{\overset{\displaystyle O}{\|}}{\underset{\underset{\displaystyle O}{\|}}{Cr}}-OH \;\longrightarrow\; R-\overset{\overset{\displaystyle R'}{|}}{\underset{\underset{\displaystyle H}{|}}{C}}-O-\overset{\overset{\displaystyle O}{\|}\,VI}{\underset{\underset{\displaystyle O}{\|}}{Cr}}-OH \;+\; H_2O$$

$$R-\overset{\overset{\displaystyle R'}{|}}{\underset{\underset{\displaystyle H}{|}}{C}}-O-\overset{\overset{\displaystyle O}{\|}}{\underset{\underset{\displaystyle O}{\|}}{Cr}}-OH \;\longrightarrow\; R-\overset{\displaystyle R'}{C}=O \;+\; {}^-O-\overset{\overset{\displaystyle O}{\|}\,IV}{Cr}-OH$$

H_2O

Aim of the Experiment

• Perform an oxidation of a secondary alcohol.

• Follow the progress of a reaction.

Learning Objectives

• Experience how chemists check on the progress of a reaction.

• Reinforcement of TLC concepts.

• Experience a biphase reaction.

• Perform an oxidation reaction; i.e., functional group modification.

Procedure

For TLC: collect two TLC plates from your TA. Prepare the developing chamber for the TLC using a 10 % ethyl acetate in hexanes[2] mixture and allow it to stabilize.

Four different solutions will be provided to you by the preproom for this experiment:

• Solution A is a 2 % borneol solution in diethyl ether

• Solution B is an aqueous solution of 5 % CrO_3 and 3.3 % sulfuric acid

• Solution C is a 10 % solution of borneol in acetone

• Solution D is 10 % camphor in acetone.

Solutions A and B (dilute) are used to run the reaction, while C and D are only used as standards for the TLC plates.

> **Safety Considerations**
> Diethyl ether is a flammable solvent and very volatile. Use caution with the other solvents too: dichloromethane is a suspected carcinogen, and methanol causes blindness and death if ingested.
>
> Chromic acid is a suspected carcinogen and an extremely corrosive strong acid. Wear gloves.

Prepare an ice water bath in a small beaker.

In a 5 mL vial, add about 1 mL of Solution A (borneol) and a magnetic stirrer. Cool to 0 °C.[3] Add about 1 mL of Solution B (oxidizing agent). Note the time of mixing, cool and shake gently to mix the two solutions. Spot a TLC with the upper layer (ether) of the reaction mixture at time 0.[4] Also spot the TLC with the two standard solutions C (borneol) and D (camphor). Shake the vial periodically to enhance the interaction between the two layers. Spot the plate again after 5 minutes reaction time, 10 minutes, 15 minutes and 20 minutes, and develop the plate. Spot the second plate again with the two standards C and D, and continue spotting the ether layer of the reaction mixture every 5 minutes for a total reaction time of about 40 minutes. Develop the second TLC plate.

Visualize the spots on the TLC plate using the $KMnO_4/K_2CO_3/NaOH$ solution. Using tongs, dip the plate into the solution, wipe the backside of the slide to remove any liquid, and place the TLC plate on a hot plate (low setting). After a few minutes, the spots will appear. Identify the borneol and camphor spots. Investigate the intensity of the borneol and camphor spots of the reaction mixture at the different time intervals. Using this information, determine the reaction time necessary for complete oxidation of borneol under your reaction conditions. Report the reaction time and the R_f values. Provide sketches of the TLC plates in your report.

Notes

1. Remember only primary and secondary alcohols can be oxidized. A tertiary alcohol is resistant to oxidation, because there are no C–H bonds involving the carbinol carbon (the carbon carrying the alcohol functionality).

2. Hexanes are an isomeric mixture of hexanes and methylcyclopentane, and somewhat cheaper than pure hexane.

3. Vials are used so we can cap them. This will minimize the evaporation of ether.

4. Spot these solutions several times to assure that enough compound is on the plate.

Discussion

•   Explain logic of experimental procedure.

•   Discuss other options for following progress of a reaction.

•   Discuss possible outcomes of oxidation reactions of alcohol as related to the structure of the alcohol and the oxidants used.

•   Describe how you would work up this reaction to isolate pure camphor.

Questions

1. Explain the difference in R_f values between borneol and camphor.

2. Write out the complete detailed mechanism for the oxidation of borneol.

3. Are the following reactions oxidations, reductions or neither?

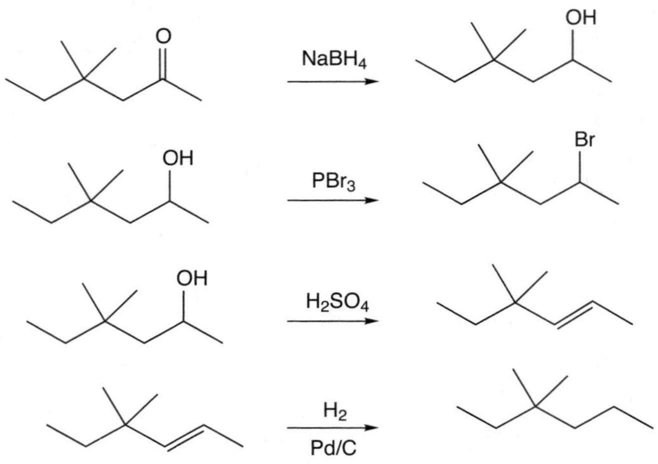

4. Describe how you would follow the Diels-Alder reaction you ran a few weeks ago by TLC. Indicate the relative order of R_f values you would expect in that specific reaction mixture.

5. A student runs the oxidation reaction of 2–hexanol, using 4.5 g of starting material and a CrO_3/H_2SO_4 mixture as the oxidant. After the reaction, the student is happy to obtain 4.1 g of crude product; however, after distillation only 2.2 g of 2–hexanone is obtained. Calculate the theoretical yield, the % yield of crude and pure product, and the % recovery in the distillation step.

6. In the oxidation reaction of borneol with CrO_3, it was necessary to periodically shake the reaction mixture. Why?

7. Describe how you would use TLC for monitoring the progress of a reaction to follow the esterification of benzoic acid with methanol to form methyl benzoate. Indicate the relative order of R_f values expected for benzoic acid and methyl benzoate.

8. A student attempted to oxidize borneol, but forgot to place it on the stir plate with a spin vane. How would this alter the reaction?

9. Why did you allow the reaction to settle before you took some of the solvent for spotting?

10. A student attempted the oxidation of borneol to camphor as suggested in the lab manual. But, as time passed, the top layer became smaller and smaller. Why might this be happening? (Ignore the fact that you spot every five minutes with some of this top layer) Why did your TA have you add more diethyl ether if you had trouble separating the two layers?

5b

Macrocyclic Synthesis (Heme Analog)

In vertebrates, two proteins, myoglobin and hemoglobin, function as oxygen carriers. Myoglobin is located in muscles where it stores and releases oxygen as necessary. Hemoglobin is present in red blood cells and is responsible for oxygen transport. Although these natural compounds are complex proteins, they both contain a non-protein part, the heme unit, that is responsible for their oxygen-carrying ability.

Hemoglobin is responsible for transporting oxygen to cells and carbon dioxide away from cells, while myoglobin is responsible for oxygen storage in the cells.[1] The heme unit is a planar macrocyclic organic molecule made up of four linked pyrrole rings surrounding an iron atom. Although the iron atom is associated with four nitrogen atoms, it can accommodate two additional ligands, one above and one below the plane of the ring. One of these positions is made available to molecular oxygen while the other helps support the heme unit by coordinating with the imidazole ring of a histidine residue in the hemoglobin protein chain.

Looking at physiological processes in the body, we notice that hemoglobin (Hb) plays a very important role. CO can bind to the ferrous ion of Hb with 200 times higher affinity than the oxygen, and forms carboxyhemoglobin. In normal circumstances, about 2 % of Hb has CO bound to it, but in CO poisoning, the increase in carboxyhemoglobin concentration makes Hb less available for oxygen and death can result if exposure is prolonged.

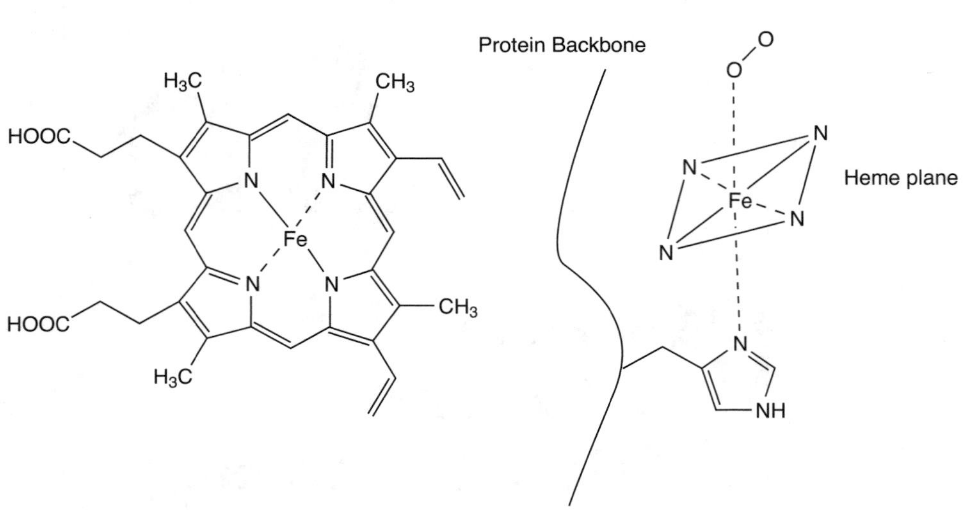

Heme is an example of a class of biologically important macrocyclic, nitrogen-containing molecules known as porphyrins. All porphyrins are able to complex metal ions. The simplest, unsubstituted porphyrin, containing 18 delocalized π–electrons, is planar, aromatic (based on Huckel [4n + 2] rule, and is given the name *porphyrin*.

The extensive conjugation system of porphyrins gives them characteristic colors, depending on their structure, substituents and the complexed metal ion. All these porphyrins have high molar absorptivity, which allow us to detect them by UV spectroscopy in very low concentrations, i.e., as low as 10^{-8} M.

This experiment illustrates a simple laboratory preparation of a porphyrin derivative, 5,10,15,20-tetraphenylporphyrin (*meso*-tetraphenylporphyrin or TPP, for short), and its copper(II), cobalt(II), or zinc(II) complex. The preparation involves the condensation of benzaldehyde with pyrrole in boiling propanoic acid. Both TPP and its copper and cobalt complexes are deeply colored solids with interesting UV/visible spectra.

Required Reading

• UV Spectroscopy in your Organic Chemistry textbook.

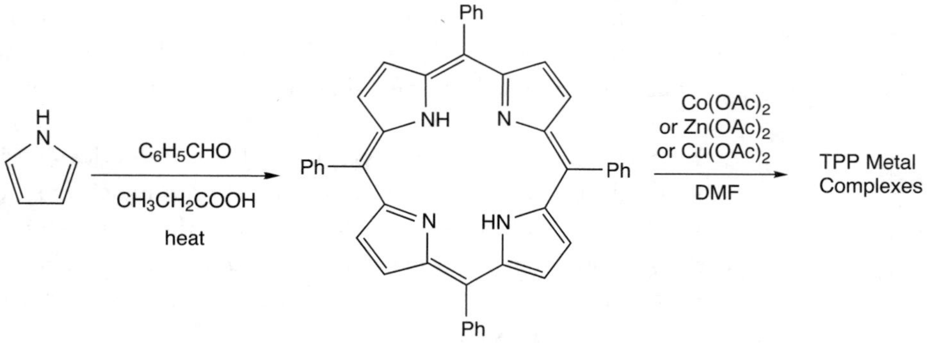

Tetraphenylporphyrin
(TPP)

Aim of the Experiment

- Synthesize a porphyrin derivative.

- Examine the effect of metal complexation.

Learning Objectives

- Macrocyclic formation versus linear polymer formation.

- Demonstrate that natural products can be made synthetically.

- Relationship between structure, UV spectroscopy, and colored compounds.

Safety Considerations

Pyrrole, methanol, and chloroform are highly flammable—keep away from hotplates and open flames. Benzaldehyde, propanoic acid, methanol, and chloroform are irritants and toxic—avoid contact with skin. Wear gloves. If contact occurs, wash with copious amounts of water and tell your instructor.

Dimethylformamide, copper(II) acetate, cobalt(II) acetate, and chloroform are irritants and toxic—avoid contact with skin. If contact occurs, wash with copious amounts of water and tell your instructor.

Procedure

Step 1. Preparation of meso-Tetraphenylporphyrin (TPP)

You will need macro glassware for this experiment. Set up a reflux apparatus, meaning a round-bottom flask with boiling chips and a reflux condenser.[2]

Place 40 mL of propanoic acid in a 250 mL round-bottomed flask, fit a reflux condenser, and bring the acid to reflux.[3] Simultaneously, add 0.7 mL (0.68 g, 10 mmol) of pyrrole and 1.0 mL (1.05 g, 10 mmol) of benzaldehyde through the condenser, using two graduated plastic syringes. Continue to heat the mixture under reflux for 30 mins.

Work-up

Cool the mixture to room temperature,[4] and collect the deeply colored product by suction filtration.[5] Filter the solution twice if necessary. Wash the product thoroughly with methanol until the methanol washings are colorless. Dry the product by suction for several minutes. Determine the % yield. Record the UV/Vis spectrum ($CHCl_3$) of the product and determine the λ_{max}.[6]

Step 2. Preparation of TPP Copper, Cobalt, or Zinc Complex

Place 10 mL of N,N-dimethylformamide (DMF) in a 25 mL Erlenmeyer flask, add a few boiling stones, and heat the flask on a hotplate until the solvent begins to boil gently. Add 100 mg (0.16 mmol) TPP to the hot DMF, and dissolve. Add approximately 40 mg (0.20 mmol) of copper(II) acetate, cobalt(II) acetate, or zinc acetate, and continue to heat the solvent at its boiling point for 5 mins.

Work-up

Cool the flask in an ice bath for about 15 mins. and then dilute the mixture with 10 mL of distilled water. Collect the solid product by suction filtration, wash it well with water, and dry by suction filtration.[7] When the product is completely dry, determine the yield and UV/Vis spectrum ($CHCl_3$) of your product, and determine the λ_{max}. If necessary, the product can be purified by column chromatography (Pasteur pipet) on alumina, eluting with chloroform.

Notes

1. Carbon monoxide binds more tightly to Fe^{+2}. Therefore, breathing CO can be fatal because it prevents the transport of oxygen.

2. Whenever you fit two glass joints together you must use a small quantity of grease as lubrication.

3. Reflux means that the solvent is boiling and recondenses in the reflux condenser. Reflux keeps the temperature of the reaction exactly at the boiling point of the solvent.

4. If you don't have a lot of crystals, you can add a little bit of methanol and continue cooling.

5. Use dichloromethane to remove residual black "stuff" from the glassware.

6. Make a dilute solution of the porphyrin products in chloroform: about 10 mL, the color should be visible but not too dark. The concentration is not very important as we are only interested in the λ_{max} for the two products. Use a small test tube (path length ~1 cm) for each solution. Also fill a test tube with pure solvent, chloroform in this case. Record a dark spectrum, a blank spectrum, i.e., solvent, and the UV spectra of the products.

7. The product tends to clog the filter paper, so "crack" the vacuum, i.e., don't apply full suction.

Discussion

• Explain logic of experimental procedure, among other aspects. Why propionic acid? Why reflux? Concentration aspect.

• Why rinse with methanol?

• Explain in your own words why λ_{max} shifts upon complexation.

• Why is TPP so stable? Why is it planar? Why does it precipitate so easily?

6b

Qualitative Analysis of Aldehydes and Ketones

Qualitative analysis of organic compounds, namely the identification of unknown samples, is an important part of organic chemistry. These identification problems can range from identifying a reaction product, for which we usually would have a very good idea of what the structure will be, to an extremely complex mixture extracted from a natural source such as tree bark or an exotic sea snail or a frog from the tropical forest. The unknown sample a chemist receives might be a pure compound, or a mixture of compounds.

The first task for a chemist receiving an unknown sample is to separate the different classes of compounds based on their solubility; for example, most organic compounds are insoluble in water, but low molecular weight alcohols and carboxylic acids are. After the separation step, the compounds have to be purified. After these procedures, a chemist is able to start with the identification procedures. Physical constants such as melting point and boiling point can be established. Spectroscopic data, such as from UV and IR spectroscopy and from NMR, can be collected. Chemical tests can also determine the nature of a certain compound, and give the chemist a clue as to the nature of the compound. As a final step in the identification process, certain derivatives can be synthesized to establish the identity of a certain compound.

In this lab we will only deal with aldehydes and ketones as unknowns, and the samples are pure compounds. This will definitely facilitate the identification of your samples. This lab will be performed by groups of students, so that you will be able to discuss your methods and results, and your options as to the identity of your unknowns. Each group of 3–4 students will be assigned a set of three unknown aldehydes and/or ketones, and should work together to obtain all the necessary data to identify these unknowns. Each student will write an individual report. Note that several opinions might exist in a group, and that not all students have to agree as to what your unknowns are.

Aim of the Experiment
- Identify unknown samples using physical constants, spectroscopic data, and diagnostic tests.

Learning Objectives
- Experience how chemists determine the identity of an unknown.

- In this case, it is limited to just aldehydes and ketones.

- Learn to work as a team to solve these problems.

- Familiarize yourself more with specific aldehydes and ketone reactions.

Required Reading
- Aldehydes and Ketones in your organic chemistry textbook

Procedure
Each group of students will receive a set of three unknowns. At least one derivative has to be synthesized for each unknown.

> **Safety Considerations**
> Many derivatives of phenylhydrazine are suspected carcinogens and should be handled with care.
>
> Tollens' reagent can form silver fulminate upon standing. Silver fulminate is very explosive, and therefore Tollens' reagent should never be stored.
>
> Nitric acid is highly corrosive. It is used to destroy the excess Tollens' reagent. Wear gloves.

A series of tests and reactions are described below. Make up a plan of action BEFORE starting the identification processes, and divide the tasks among the group members. It is suggested that one student act as the "manager" and one as the "secretary." It is also suggested that some preliminary data are collected about the unknowns, such as mp, IR spectra, and simple diagnostic tests, and that the group then meet to discuss strategy.

If an unknown is a solid, a melting point should be taken. IR spectra should be run on all unknowns.

For liquids, you can determine the boiling point using the procedure described in *Making the Connections.*

Some of the tests described below will determine if you have an aldehyde or ketone, which should help you in the identification process. For each test, three experiments should be run simultaneously: on a compound known to give a positive test, on a compound known to give a negative test, and on your unknown. Working in this way will help you distinguish positive from negative tests, and if the reagents are working as they should.

After you have done the identification tests, a derivative has to be synthesized of your unknown. The melting point of the derivative will help you identify your unknown. The results of the IR and the identifying tests may suggest derivatives whose melting points will be particularly revealing.

> **Caution**
> Please make sure you don't contaminate the reagents with other chemicals as this leads to false results for the whole class.

Infrared Spectroscopy
Run IR spectra on all your unknowns. Determine if you might have an aldehyde or a ketone, and check for additional functional groups, such as C=C or aromatic groups.

Tollens' Test
This is a test for aldehydes. Aldehydes are very easily oxidized to the corresponding carboxylic acid, in this case using a silver salt. Ag^+ will be reduced to metallic Ag, resulting in a silver mirror in the test tube.

Possible test substances for this test are benzophenone (negative) and benzaldehyde or another aldehyde (positive). Acetone can actually give false positives here, so make sure your test tubes are free of acetone.

Place a few mL of 10 % aqueous NaOH in 4–5 clean test tubes and heat them in a water bath while preparing Tollens' reagent. This step is meant to remove all acidic impurities from the test tubes.

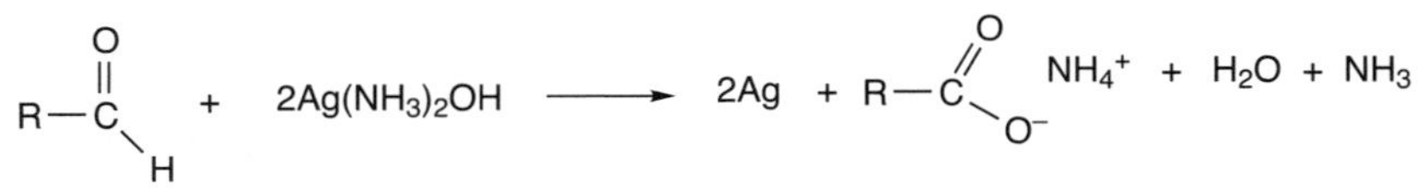

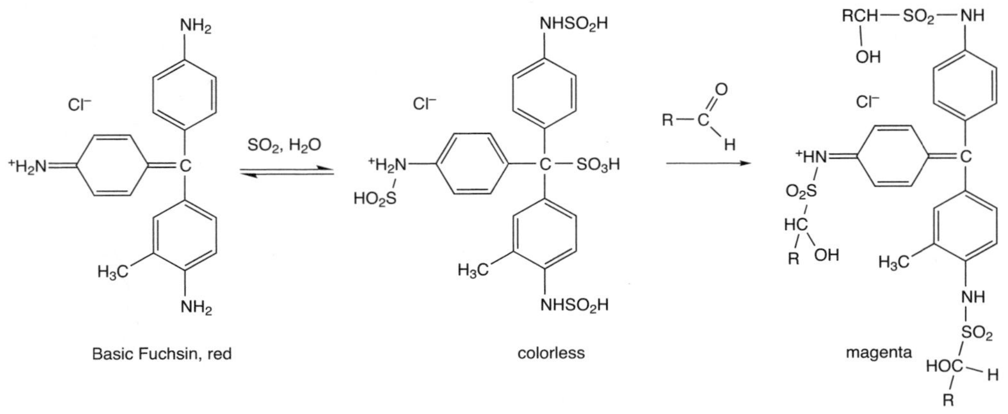

Basic Fuchsin, red

colorless

magenta

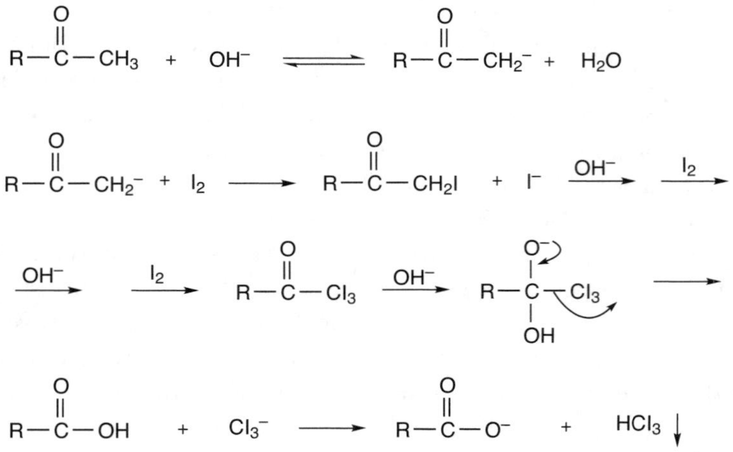

To 1 mL of Tollens' solution A (5 % aqueous silver nitrate[1]) in a test tube, add 0.5 mL of Tollens' solution B (10 % NaOH in water). A gray precipitate of silver oxide (Ag_2O) will form, and enough 10 % aqueous ammonia should be added to dissolve the silver oxide. Shake the mixture. Dilute this solution to about 5 mL. This mixture should be prepared just before doing the test.

Empty the test tubes of NaOH solution, rinse them with water, and add 0.5 mL of Tollens' reagent to each. Add ONE drop of the substance to be tested by allowing it to run down the inside of the test tube, or add ~10 mg in the case of a solid. Set the tubes aside for a few minutes without shaking. If no reaction occurs, warm the mixture briefly in the water bath. A positive test consists of the formation of a silver mirror in the test tube.

Waste disposal: Make the remaining Tollens' reagent acidic by adding nitric acid, then neutralize the solution with sodium carbonate and dispose of the solution in the waste bottle.

Schiff's Test

This is another way of distinguishing aldehydes from ketones. Schiff's reagent is a solution of the red dye Basic Fuchsin, which is rendered colorless on treatment with sulfur dioxide. In the presence of an aldehyde the colorless solution turns magenta.

Add 1 drop of unknown to 0.7 mL of Schiff's reagent and slightly heat the solution. A magenta color will appear within 10 minutes for aldehydes. Compare to the colors produced by a known ketone and a known aldehyde. Benzaldehyde doesn't work as well as other aldehydes due to its low solubility.

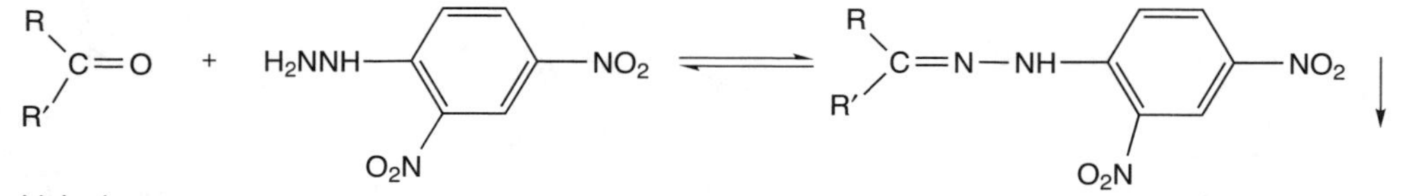

aldehyde or ketone

2,4–dinitrophenylhydrazine

2,4–dinitrophenylhydrazone

Iodoform Test

The iodoform test allows us to distinguish methyl ketones from other ketones. Iodoform CHI_3 is formed as a yellow crystalline solid of mp 119–123 °C.[2,3] In this test a methyl ketone is treated with iodine in a basic solution. The α-hydrogens are acidic and the enolate anion is formed, which reacts with the elemental iodine. Introduction of the first iodine in the α-position increases the acidity of the remaining α-hydrogens and the triiodo compound is formed. CI_3^- is a very good leaving group, and subsequent protonation leads to the formation of iodoform.

The reagent contains iodine in a potassium iodide solution at such a concentration that reaction of 0.75 mL of this solution with an excess methyl ketone will yield 43 mg of iodoform. If the substance to be tested is water-soluble, dissolve 1 drop of the liquid or ~15 mg of a solid unknown in 0.5 mL of water in a test tube. Add 0.5 mL of 10 % aqueous NaOH and then, slowly, 0.75 mL of the iodine solution. If the substance is not soluble in water, dissolve it in 0.5 mL 1,2-dimethoxyethane (glyme) and proceed as above, and dilute with 2.5 mL of water at the end. Shake the CORKED test tube vigorously. It may be necessary to heat the solution slightly in a warm water bath to aid in the disappearance of the color. In a positive test the brown color of the iodine disappears and yellow iodoform separates. It may take 15 minutes for the iodoform to precipitate out. Collect the iodoform and determine its melting point (lit. 119–123 °C). Use acetone as a test substance.

2,4–Dinitrophenylhydrazones

Amines are good nucleophiles and readily add to the carbonyl group. Intermediate hydroxyamines form, which are not stable. Mildly acidic conditions will result in a dehydration and formation of the corresponding imine, commonly referred to as a Schiff base. 2,4–Dinitrophenylhydrazine and semicarbazide form useful stable imines; they are solids and helpful in the characterization of aldehydes and ketones. Liquid aldehydes and ketones will yield crystalline imine derivatives with sharp melting points, which can be used in identification. In addition the molecular weight increases dramatically, resulting in easily isolable quantities of the derivatives.[4]

Place ten drops of a liquid unknown in a test tube with 1 mL of methanol, and add dropwise (up to 3 mL if needed) of the 2,4-dinitrophenylhydrazine solution.[5] If the unknown is a solid, first dissolve about 100 mg in 1 mL of methanol (minimal amount). Shake the reaction mixture vigorously. Warm the reaction mixture for a few minutes in a water bath and allow to stand for 15–30 minutes to let the crystallization proceed. (Add water if the mixture remains cloudy.) Collect the product by filtration,[6] and wash the crystals with a large amount of water. Test the acidity of the crystals by pressing a moist piece of litmus paper onto the crystals. Continue rinsing until the crystals are neutral. Dry the product as much as possible by pressing it between filter paper. Recrystallize from ethanol-water, and ethyl acetate for less soluble materials. Dry. Determine the melting point.

Compound	mp	bp	2,4–DNP mp	Semicarbazone mp
Acetone		56	126	187
Propanal		48	148	89
Butanal		75	123	95
Furfural		161	212(230)[a]	202
Heptanal		156	108	109
Benzaldehyde		179	237	222
m–Nitrobenzaldehyde	58		293	246
4–Methylbenzaldehyde		204	234	234
trans-Cinnamaldehyde		252	255	215
Vanilin	80	285(d)[b]	271(d)[b]	229
Terephthalaldehyde	116	245		154(278 di)[c]
2–Butanone		80	117	146
3–Pentanone		102	156	138
Hexane–2,5–dione		191	257(di)[c]	185(224di)[c]
2–Heptanone		151	89	123
Pinacolone		106	125	157
Cyclohexanone		155	162	166
Acetophenone		200	238	198
Benzophenone	48	305	238	167
(±) Camphor	179	205	177	237
Benzil	95	347	189(di)[c]	175(244di)[c]

a. *Melting point can be different depending on the crystal structure.*
b. *d = Decomposes.*
c. *Both functional groups can be derivatized, leading to a diderivative.*

Semicarbazones

Semicarbazone derivatives are also very stable, crystalline and useful in structure determination of unknowns. Because semicarbazide itself (H_2N–NH–CO–NH_2) is not very stable in its free form, it is usually used as its hydrochloride salt. A base, namely pyridine, is then added to the reaction mixture to free the semicarbazide *in situ*.

To 1 mL of the aqueous semicarbazide hydrochloride solution, add ~80 mg of the compound to be tested and enough methanol to produce a clear solution. Add 5 drops of pyridine and warm the solution gently in a water bath for a few minutes. Cool the solution slowly to room temperature. It might be necessary to scratch the inside of the test tube to induce crystallization. Cool the test tube in ice water and filter the product. Wash with cold methanol. Recrystallize from methanol, ethanol or ethanol/water. Determine the melting point.

aldehyde or ketone   semicarbazide hydrochloride   pyridine   semicarbazone

Notes

1. Keep the $AgNO_3$ solutions off your hands. The Ag^+ oxidizes to Ag metal in the atmosphere, which results in black spots. These are not harmful; they just look bad.

2. Notice the similar structure of iodoform CHI_3 and chloroform $CHCl_3$.

3. Acetaldehyde will give a positive iodoform test, as it is both an aldehyde and a methyl ketone.

4. Read your organic chemistry textbook for detailed description of the imine formation.

5. The solution contains 2,4–dinitrophenyl-hydrazine and sulfuric acid in methanol.

6. Centrifuge if the crystalline deposit is too fine to filter.

Discussion

• Present the results obtained by the group. What results were obtained?

• Present your arguments and reasoning to defend your conclusion as to what your unknowns are. Convince your TA with your arguments.

• If you know some other students have a different opinion, why do you think your conclusion is correct?

• The important thing is to present logical and defendable arguments.

Questions

1. The following mp data were obtained by doing four derivative tests.

Compound	Test A	Test B	Test C	Test D
Benzoic acid	92	132	115	80
Hexanoic acid	101	131	110	133
3–Hexenoic acid	141	135	148	78
3–Methyl–benzoic acid	95	129	150	83

a. Which two derivative tests are you going to choose to differentiate between these four compounds?

b. Given melting points of 92, 129, 148, and 80 °C for derivatives A, B, C, and D respectively, what is the unknown acid?

2. In the IR spectra, how would you differentiate between an aldehyde or a ketone, since they both have carbonyls?

3. Explain the different colors observed in the Schiff's test.

7b

Aldol Condensation

The formation of carbon–carbon bonds is very important in synthetic organic chemistry. The Diels-Alder reaction performed in one of the previous labs is one example of a reaction which very efficiently builds up six-membered rings by forming new carbon–carbon bonds. In this lab we will study the aldol condensation which takes advantage of the reactivity of the carbonyl functionality to build new carbon–carbon bonds.

The main characteristic of a carbonyl functionality is its dipolar character. Oxygen is more electronegative than carbon, resulting in the polarization of the carbon–oxygen π–bond. If we investigate the possible resonance forms for the carbonyl function, we conclude that this polarization arises from the contribution of the zwitterionic resonance hybrid.

This polarization results in the ability of the carbonyl group to undergo a variety of reactions. The carbonyl carbon, which is $\delta+$, is susceptible to attack by nucleophiles, which leads to many reactions. Among them are the aldol condensation, the Wittig reaction, and Grignard reaction, just to name a few.

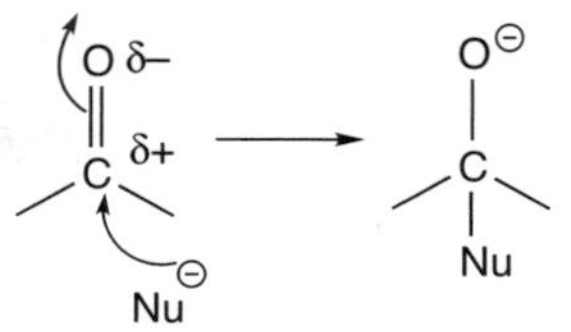

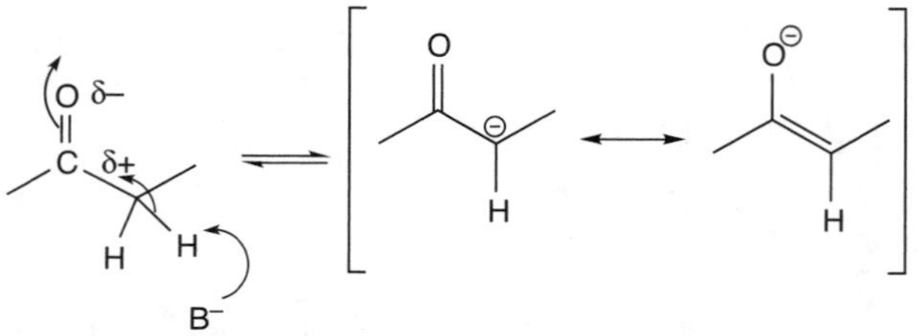

Studying the structure of a carbonyl compound a little further, it becomes obvious that the δ+ charge on the carbonyl carbon also affects the neighboring hydrogens. The α–hydrogens will become more acidic due to the presence of the carbonyl functionality for two reasons: inductively the hydrogens will be more acidic because of the δ+ charge, and in addition, the conjugate base after deprotonation will be stabilized by resonance to the enolate anion.

In the aldol condensation, these two possible reaction pathways for the carbonyl compound are combined: an enolate is formed from one carbonyl compound which then acts as a nucleophile to attack another carbonyl compound. Applying this, for example, to acetaldehyde, reaction of base with acetaldehyde results in

the acetaldehyde enolate which then attacks the carbonyl carbon of another molecule of acetaldehyde. The product is an aldehyde–alcohol derivative, therefore the name aldol, which can then dehydrate (expulsion of water) to form an α, β–unsaturated aldehyde, crotonaldehyde in this case.

The initially formed aldol product will sometimes spontaneously dehydrate, but other times it won't. The dehydration is more favored if the product formed has extended conjugation, and/or if the dehydration product precipitates out of solution.

Mixed or crossed aldol condensations refer to the cases in which two different carbonyl compounds are the reactants. In most cases this

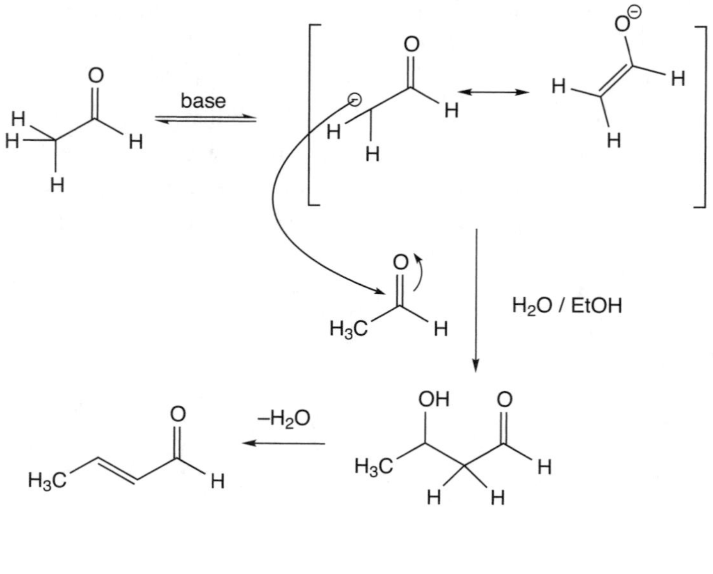

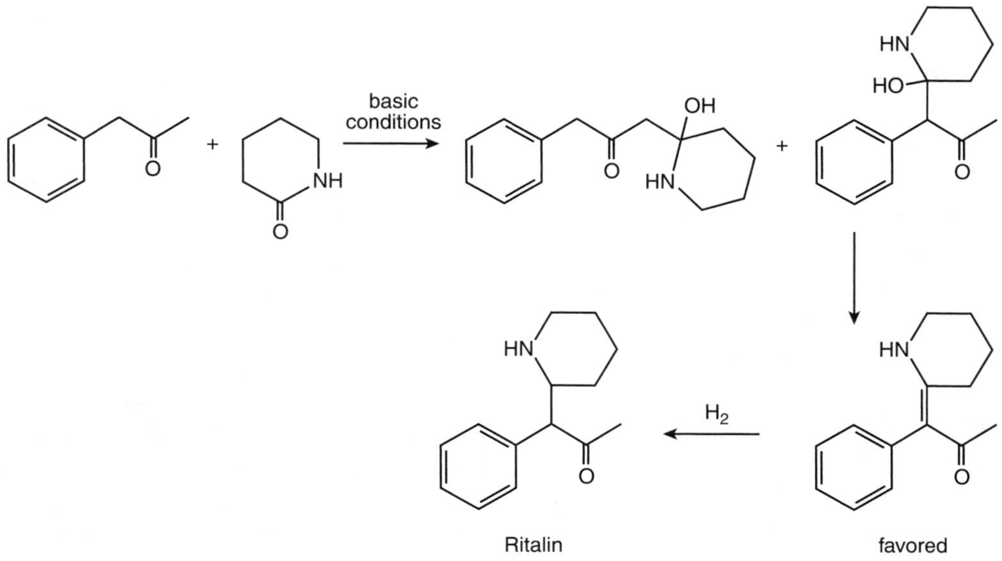

Ritalin   favored

Ritalin

will lead to a mixture of products. However, in some cases a mixed aldol condensation can lead to a single major product. One such case occurs when one of the carbonyl compounds has no α-hydrogens, as for example in benzaldehyde.

Double aldol condensations are also possible. An example of this is the case of reaction of a symmetric ketone; i.e., acetone, will be able to react with two molecules of another carbonyl compound under alkaline conditions.

An example of an aldol condensation from the pharmaceutical industry is the synthesis of Ritalin. Ritalin is a medication prescribed for individuals, usually children, who have attention-deficit hyperactivity disorder (ADHD). ADHD consists of a persistent pattern of abnormally high levels of activity, impulsivity, and/or inattention that is more frequently displayed and more severe than is typically observed in individuals with comparable levels of development. This medication is often abused by college students because of its ability to help one focus. Reaction of 1-phenyl-propan-2-one with 2-piperidone under basic conditions gives a fully dehydrated aldol product. Interestingly, two aldol products are possible. The protons

of the terminal methyl group are more acidic, so you would expect the aldol to occur there preferentially, but the dehydrated product of the other aldol is more highly conjugated and therefore more stable. Simple hydrogenation of the aldol product leads to Ritalin.

Required Reading
- Aldol condensation in your Organic Chemistry textbook

- Recrystallization

Aim of the Experiment
- Perform aldol condensation of different ketones.

- Recrystallize the product from a suitable solvent.

- Identify the product by IR and NMR.

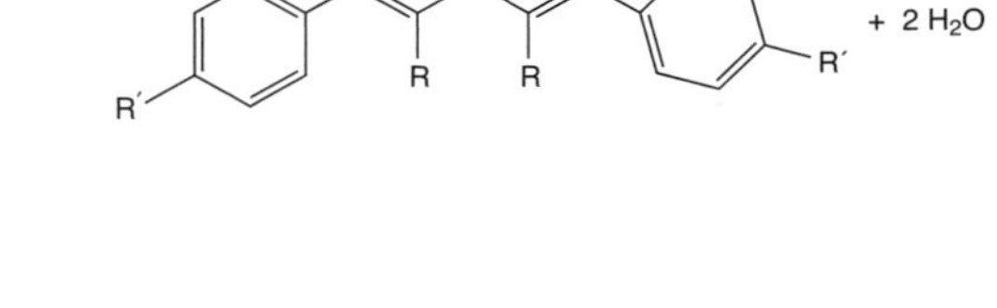

Learning Objectives

- Learn about aldol condensation and dehydration.

- Learn to make decisions about solvents in recrystallization.

- Reexposure to the importance of NMR spectroscopy for identification purposes.

Experimental Background

Students will perform a double aldol condensation with a pair of the following list of starting materials. The available ketones include acetone, cyclohexanone and cyclopentanone. The available aldehydes include benzaldehyde, *p*-tolualdehyde (*p*-methylbenzaldehyde), and cinnamaldehyde (E-3-phenyl-2-propenal).

The following factors influence these reactions:

- The ketones are less reactive than aldehydes in aldol condensations, because the carbonyl group of ketones is sterically and electronically not as susceptible to nucleophilic attack as is the carbonyl function of aldehydes.

- The aldehydes used have no α–hydrogens and therefore cannot react with themselves.

- The ketones are symmetric and will undergo the aldol condensation twice.

- The product is highly conjugated and therefore the hydration will be very facile.

The melting points of the products are given in the table below.

> **Safety Considerations**
>
> Aldehydes and ketones are usually skin and eye irritants.
>
> Aqueous sodium hydroxide solutions are corrosive and cause burns. Rinse with water for at least 15 minutes if spilled on the skin.

Procedure

Your instructor will assign you a pair of starting materials.

Using a syringe, measure 0.8 mL of the aldehyde derivative in a preweighed 25 mL Erlenmeyer flask. Weigh the flask. After cleaning the syringe, add 0.2 mL of the ketone derivative in the Erlenmeyer, and weigh again. Add 4.0 mL of 95 % ethanol and 3 mL of 2 M sodium hydroxide solution. Stir the solution for 15 minutes with a magnetic stirrer. Stir longer if precipitate is still forming. If the solution is still cloudy, or if very little precipitate has formed, heat the reaction mixture in a hot water bath (~80 °C) for 10–15 minutes. Cool the flask to room temperature.

Table: Melting points of double aldol condensation product.

	Acetone	**Cyclohexanone**	**Cyclopentanone**
Benzaldehyde	113 °C	118 °C	189 °C
p–Tolualdehyde	175 °C	170 °C	235 °C
Cinnamaldehyde	144 °C	180 °C	235 °C

Work-up

Cool the flask in ice water.

In two test tubes place 8 mL of 95 % ethanol and 4 mL of 4 % acetic acid in 95 % ethanol (v/v) respectively. Chill the content of these two tubes in the ice bath.

Collect the product using vacuum filtration. Rinse the product with half of the chilled ethanol, then with the acetic acid/ethanol solution, and finally with the remainder of the chilled ethanol. Recrystallize the product from a suitable solvent. The solvents available to you include toluene, 95 % ethanol, acetone, and hexanes. Deionized water is, of course, always available.

Filter the crystals and allow them to dry on top of the filter.

Determine yield and the melting point. Record an IR spectrum and submit your sample for NMR.

Selecting a Recrystallization Solvent

- Place about 50 mg of the sample in a test tube.

- Add about 0.5 mL of a solvent at room temperature, and stir the mixture by twirling the test tube. If most of the solid dissolves, then your product is too soluble in this solvent. Repeat the procedure with a less polar solvent.

- If none or very few of the crystals dissolve at room temperature, heat the test tube in a hot water bath. Add more solvent if necessary to dissolve the crystals. Don't add more than 1.5 mL. If the crystals don't dissolve in refluxing solvent, repeat the procedure with a more polar solvent.

- If the crystals dissolved, allow the solution to cool to room temperature and then place it in an ice bath. If lots of crystals develop, you have found a good solvent.

Comments

- Picking a good solvent is something of an art. There is no perfect procedure, only trial and error, accompanied by reasoning and common sense.

- Feel free to mix these solvents in any ratio to achieve the best recrystallization medium for your compound.

- Hexane is sometimes added to help the crystals to form.

- Patience is a good thing, and makes for very nice crystals.

Discussion

- Discuss the mechanism of the specific aldol condensation that you performed.

- Discuss the reasoning you used to choose the solvent for recrystallization.

- Discuss the spectral data and how they confirm the identity of your product.

Questions

1. Complete the mechanism of the aldol condensation of acetaldehyde given above. Not all details are shown in the scheme above.

2. To undergo aldol condensation with itself, a carbonyl compound has to have at least one α–hydrogen. Indicate if the following have α–hydrogens. If yes, give the aldol condensation product. a. acetone, b. 3–pentanone, c. acetophenone, d. formaldehyde, e. benzophenone, d. cyclohexanone.

3. Aldol condensations are equilibrium reactions, therefore Le Châtelier's principle applies. This principle is explained in the Fischer esterification experiment. Show how Le Châtelier's principle can be used to increase the yield of the reaction you did in this lab.

4. Still on Le Châtelier's principle: ketones are known to be less reactive in aldol condensations. Why? In view of this, how can the aldol condensation of acetone be manipulated to obtain a reasonable yield of product?

5. Show the possible side product of the mixed aldol condensation you did in this lab. Hint: self-condensation is always possible if α-hydrogens are present.

6. Mixing acetone with butanal in the presence of base leads to a variety of products. List all possible products.

8b

FAME, Analysis of Fats and Oils

The bulk of plant and animal tissue is composed of three main classes of compounds: carbohydrates, proteins, and lipids. The term "lipid" includes all substances in living tissues that are soluble in ether, methylene chloride or similar organic solvents. The most abundant lipids are triesters of glycerol (glycerine = $HOCH_2–CH(OH)–CH_2OH$) with long-chain "fatty" acids. The triesters, or triglycerides, from animal sources are usually low-melting solids and are called fats, while those from plants are viscous oils that solidify below 0 °C. The general structures are the same, and the difference in properties occurs because the vegetable oils contain a larger proportion of unsaturated fatty acid chains, with one, two, or three double bonds in the chain. Triglycerides such as beef tallow and other fats of animals contain mostly acid chains without double bonds. The bent chains which result from incorporating cis-alkene groups into a chain prevent close packing in a solid and, as a result, such molecules exhibit lower melting points. For example, compare oleic acid (C_{18} with one double bond, mp 4 °C) with its saturated analogue, stearic acid (mp 69 °C). The degree of unsaturation is important in nutrition, since there is evidence that a high proportion of saturated fats in the diet leads to deposition of cholesterol in blood vessels (atherosclerosis).

Fatty acids almost invariably have chains with an **even** number of carbon atoms, most commonly 16 or 18. A few of the more important fatty acids are listed in Table 1.

Table 1. Typical fatty acids.

#C	#DB	Name	Structure
12	0	lauric	$CH_3(CH_2)_{10}COOH$
14	0	myristic	$CH_3(CH_2)_{12}COOH$
16	0	palmitic	$CH_3(CH_2)_{14}COOH$
18	0	stearic	$CH_3(CH_2)_{16}COOH$
16	1	palmitoleic	$CH_3(CH_2)_5CH=CH(CH_2)_7COOH$
18	1	oleic	$CH_3(CH_2)_7CH=CH(CH_2)_7COOH$
18	2	linoleic	$CH_3(CH_2)_4CH=CHCH_2CH=CH(CH_2)_7COOH$
18	3	linolenic	$CH_3CH_2CH=CHCH_2CH=CHCH_2CH=CH(CH_2)_7COOH$

#C = number of carbon atoms
#DB = number of double bonds

Table 2. Typical percentages of fatty acids in selected fats and oils.
% Constituent fatty acids.

# Carbon Atoms	<12	12	14	16	16	18	18	18	18	>18
# Double Bonds	0	0	0	0	1	0	1	2	3	
Human fat	-	-	3	24	5	8	47	10	-	2
Butterfat	4	4	12	33	2	12	29	2	-	2
Lard	-	-	1	28	1	16	43	9	-	2
Coconut oil	15	46	18	10	-	4	6	-	-	-
Corn oil	-	-	-	10	1	2	25	62	-	-
Cottonseed oil	-	-	1	20	2	1	20	55	-	1
Linseed oil	-	-	-	10	-	4	23	57	6	-
Olive oil	-	-	-	9	-	3	78	10	-	-
Palm oil	-	-	1	45	-	4	40	10	-	-
Peanut oil	-	-	-	10	-	3	48	34	-	5
Safflower oil	-	-	-	7	-	2	13	75	3	-
Soybean oil	-	-	-	9	-	4	43	40	4	-

These and several others can occur in any combination in a given triglyceride. The compositions of a few fats and oils are given in Table 2. These values vary over a fairly wide range, depending on the source of the fat or oil, and there is no one "correct" set of values. Butterfat and coconut oil are atypical, since the mixtures of acids in these triglycerides contain a significant number of 8–, 10–, and 12–carbon chains.

From these approximate compositions of different fats and oils, you can easily determine which one are the "healthy" oils and the "unhealthy" ones. Remember the recent publicity surrounding the use of palm oil in making popcorn in movie theaters, containing 45 % fully saturated palmitic acid, compared to corn oil which contains mostly unsaturated C_{18} fatty acids.

In this procedure the oils or fats (triglycerides) are saponified to the carboxylate, and in acidic conditions, the acid is esterified by methanol/$AlCl_3$ mixture. The methyl esters can then be identified and quantified by gas chromatographic analysis. This is the actual procedure used in the food industry to analyze fats and oils.

Required Reading
• Fatty acids and Triglycerides in your Organic Chemistry textbook.

Aim of the Experiment
• Perform a saponification followed by an esterification.

• Apply an analysis technique used in the food industry.

• Identify the fat based on gas chromatography data.

Learning Objectives
• Perform saponification of a fat, followed by a methyl ester formation.

• Work up this complex reaction mixture.

• Analyze the methyl ester by gas chromatography.

Procedure
A group of students will be working on the identification of a given unknown oil. The transesterification is a fast reaction, and standards for the GCs and the mixture of standards should be available. An example of a GC of the standards is shown on the next page. Note that the standard mixture does not contain methyl oleate, because it has the same retention time as methyl stearate. Each student will generate their own lab report, including copies of all the GC chromatograms.

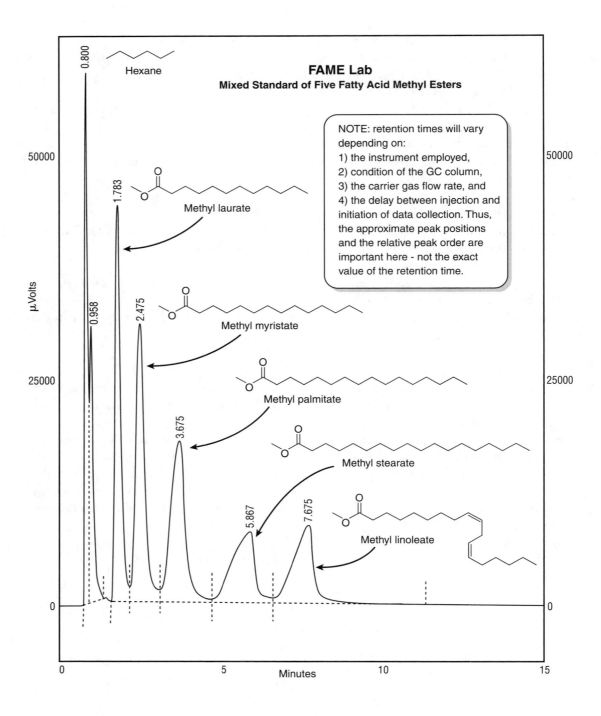

FAME Lab
Mixed Standard of Five Fatty Acid Methyl Esters

NOTE: retention times will vary depending on:
1) the instrument employed,
2) condition of the GC column,
3) the carrier gas flow rate, and
4) the delay between injection and initiation of data collection. Thus, the approximate peak positions and the relative peak order are important here - not the exact value of the retention time.

PART A: *Transesterification of the Fat*

Thoroughly clean and dry a 100 mL round-bottom flask and a reflux condenser. Pipet 0.15–0.20 g of the oil into the flask. Add 2.5 mL of 1 M methanolic sodium hydroxide. Connect the reflux condenser and heat the reaction mixture, using a water bath, until the fat globules have dissolved. This usually requires 3–5 minutes. Cool the flask to room temperature. Avoid breathing the fumes.

Add 3 mL of 10 % (wt/v) $AlCl_3$ in methanol to the flask. Equip the flask with a reflux condenser and heat the mixture for 3–5 minutes. Cool to room temperature.

Work-up

Transfer the mixture to a small separatory funnel using 15 mL of hexanes, and wash the organic layer with 10 mL of saturated aqueous sodium chloride solution. Don't shake the separatory funnel, because this mixture has a great tendency to form emulsions. Instead, gently swirl the contents of the funnel and be patient. Most of the methanol will be in the aqueous layer. Drain and discard the water layer (bottom layer) and dry the organic layer over $MgSO_4$. Filter the dried solution by suction filtration and evaporate the solvent until dry. Add 2 drops of hexanes to redissolve the methyl esters. Transfer to a vial to go inject in the GC.

PART B: *Analysis by Gas Chromatography (GC) of the Transesterification Products*

Check and record the GC used and computer settings in your notebook. *Please do not change the settings yourself.* Rinse the syringe with a small amount of hexane and then use it to inject a sample into the 10 % Silar column. The amount of sample to inject will depend on the concentration of your sample; inject ~1 μL. Don't forget to hit the trigger to start the computer. Rinse the syringe again with a small amount of hexane. Remember that the first peak should be hexane. When in doubt consult your TA. Make sure you NEVER inject a second sample on a column when a sample had already been injected less than 15 minutes beforehand.

Discussion

• Explain the reaction conditions.

• Discuss the alternative route of direct transesterification.

• Explain the logic of the extraction procedure.

• Discuss the results obtained from GC analysis.

• Defend your identification of the oil you analyzed.

Questions

1. Why was $AlCl_3$ used in the experiment? (Show mechanism)

2. If you inject a sample of methyl laurate, C_{12} and no double bonds, and methyl oleate, C_{18} and 1 double bond, which would you expect to come off the GC first and why?

3. Write out a stepwise mechanism for the acid-catalyzed trans-esterification below.

$$\text{ethyl propanoate + methanol} \xrightarrow{\text{HCl}} \text{methyl propanoate}$$

4. Why was water added to the solution after refluxing? Write out a balanced chemical equation for what happens. Why should this be done in the hood? Why was magnesium sulfate $(MgSO_4)$ or sodium sulfate added to the organic layer?

5. A student took an unknown compound and reacted it with chlorine gas in the presence of a UV lamp. He obtained two products when the sample was analyzed by GC. The chromatograph from the GC contained 3 peaks. Two of the peaks were overlapping, while the first peak corresponded to the starting material. Similar problems were encountered in the FAME experiment.
   a. How might the two peaks that were overlapping be resolved better?
   b. If more sample was injected, would the retention time change for any of the three peaks? Why or why not?
   c. Draw the chromatogram obtained for the GC if the products bp were 40 and 42 °C.
   d. Upon elemental analysis and mass spectroscopy, the student discovered that one of the products contained three chlorines ($C_4H_5Cl_3$, bp 40 °C), while the other product had two chlorines ($C_4H_6Cl_2$, bp 42 °C). The product with two chlorines was analyzed by proton nmr, resulting in the following information:
   singlet, 3H, at 2.2 ppm
   doublet, 2H, at 4.1 ppm
   triplet, 1H, at 5.7 ppm
   What is the structure of the product? (Hint: calculate the "unsaturation" value.)
   e. What was the unknown starting material?

9b

Multistep Synthesis of Tetraphenylcyclopentadienone

In the Diels-Alder reaction, you have already been exposed to a two-step synthesis, with the second step being rather simple, namely the hydrolysis of the anhydride functionality. Syntheses in research laboratories and pharmaceutical plants, for example, very often consist of more than five steps, sometimes more than 20 steps for very intricate molecules such as taxol and prostaglandines. To just give you a flavor of the problems involved in multistep syntheses, you will perform a three-step synthesis sequence to obtain tetraphenylcyclopentadienone. The most obvious problem of course is that you have to produce enough material in the first step to make it to the end. Remember that hardly any reactions proceed in 100 % yield, which means that the amount of product diminishes as you go ahead in a reaction sequence. In synthetic labs it is not uncommon to start with kg quantities to end up with just a few mg at the end, barely enough to record a NMR spectrum to confirm the structure of the material.

Starting from benzaldehyde, you will synthesize tetraphenylcyclopentadienone. In this experiment the student has to obtain the desired product at the end. If one of the synthesis steps fails, the student has to repeat the experiment or "buy" the necessary intermediate for 10 points. All intermediates have to be characterized, the melting point has to be measured and IR spectrum recorded.

tetraphenylcyclopentadienone

Benzaldehyde is treated with a weak nucleophile leading to a dimeric product benzoin. Benzoin is oxidized to benzil, and the latter is treated with 1,3-diphenylacetone (1,3-diphenyl-2-propanone) in the presence of base to lead to the desired product, tetraphenylcyclopentadienone. The reaction sequence is shown in the scheme above.

Reaction Mechanisms

The most common reaction of aldehydes and ketones is nucleophilic attack at the highly polarized carbonyl group. These reactions include formation of cyanohydrins, formation of acetals, addition of sulfur nucleophiles, formation of imines, and the aldol reaction. In an aldol condensation, the enolate anion of a carbonyl compound formed in alkaline conditions reacts with the carbonyl group of the same or a different compound. Aldol condensations however cannot occur with aldehydes and ketones without α-hydrogens, because the enolate anion cannot form.

Benzaldehyde does not possess α-hydrogens and therefore does not undergo an aldol condensation.[1] The benzoin condensation is unique to benzaldehyde, and was originally found to occur when benzaldehyde was mixed with cyanide anion, a nucleophile. To avoid the use of the highly toxic sodium cyanide, we are using thiamine (vitamin B1) instead. Thiamine itself is rather unstable, but its hydrochloride salt is very stable and inexpensive. The thiazolium ion[2] is generated in situ by the addition of base. The free thiamine is bright yellow in basic conditions, and almost colorless in acidic conditions, so that it can act as an acid–base indicator. In order to be nucleophilic enough, the thiamine has to be completely liberated from its salt, so the solution has to be bright yellow for the reaction to occur. However, the thiamine is base labile and is readily decomposed by heat at a pH of 5.5 or higher. Therefore, we have to control the pH and temperature very carefully.

In the first step, the thiamine carbanion attacks the carbonyl group of benzaldehyde, forming a formal oxy anion. A hydrogen shift leads to another very reaction carbanion, which attacks a second benzaldehyde molecule. Another hydrogen shift followed by expulsion of the thiamine catalyst leads to the benzoin compound.

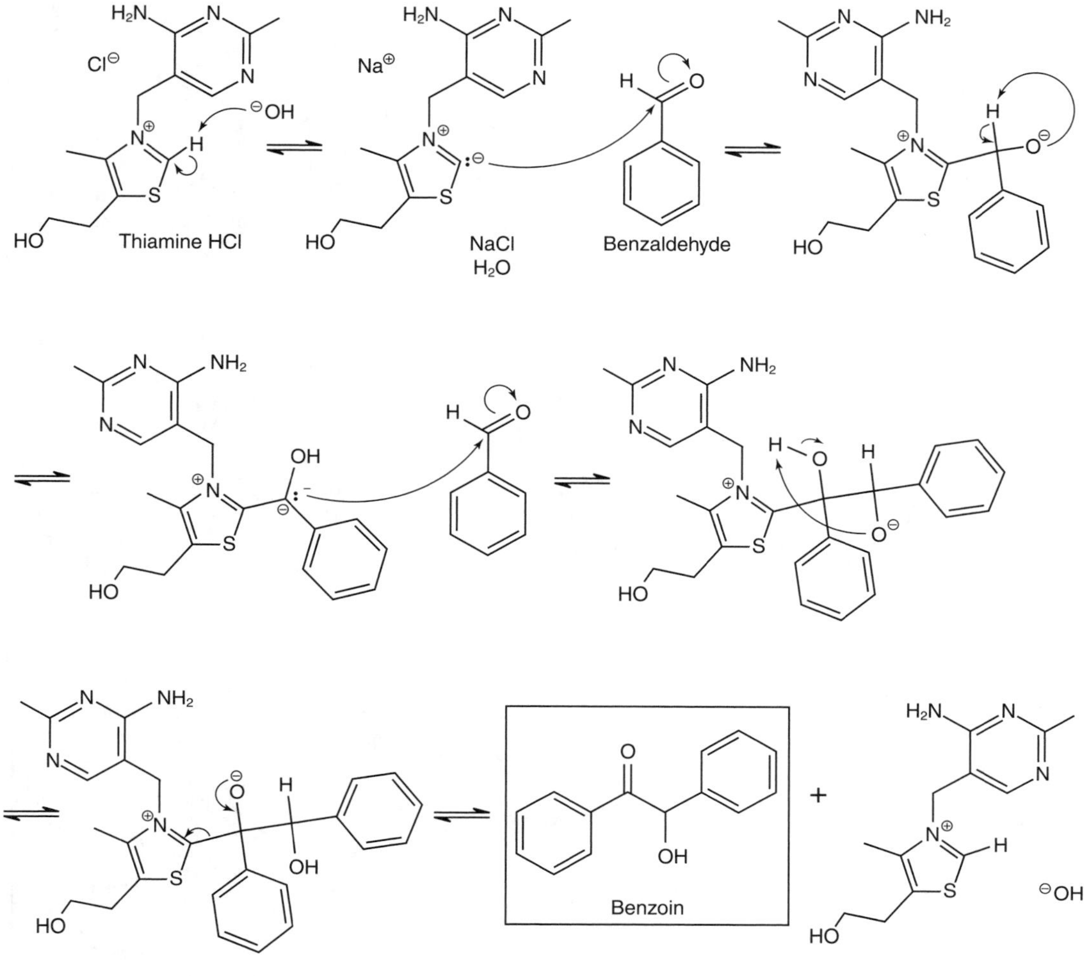

Thiamine HCl

NaCl
H₂O

Benzaldehyde

Benzoin

The second step in the reaction sequence is the oxidation of benzoin to benzil. This is a simple oxidation of an alcohol function to the corresponding carbonyl function, performed in this instance with nitric acid as the oxidizing agent.

The third step in the sequence is a double aldol condensation, accompanied by dehydration, leading to the highly conjugated tetraphenyl-cyclopentadienone. In alkaline conditions, the enolate anion of 1,3-diphenylacetone is formed.[3] Attack on benzil leads to a first aldol condensation product, which then undergoes a second, now intramolecular, aldol condensation. The second aldol condensation product readily undergoes dehydration to form the highly conjugated purple end product.

Required Reading

• Aldol condensation

• Oxidation of alcohols

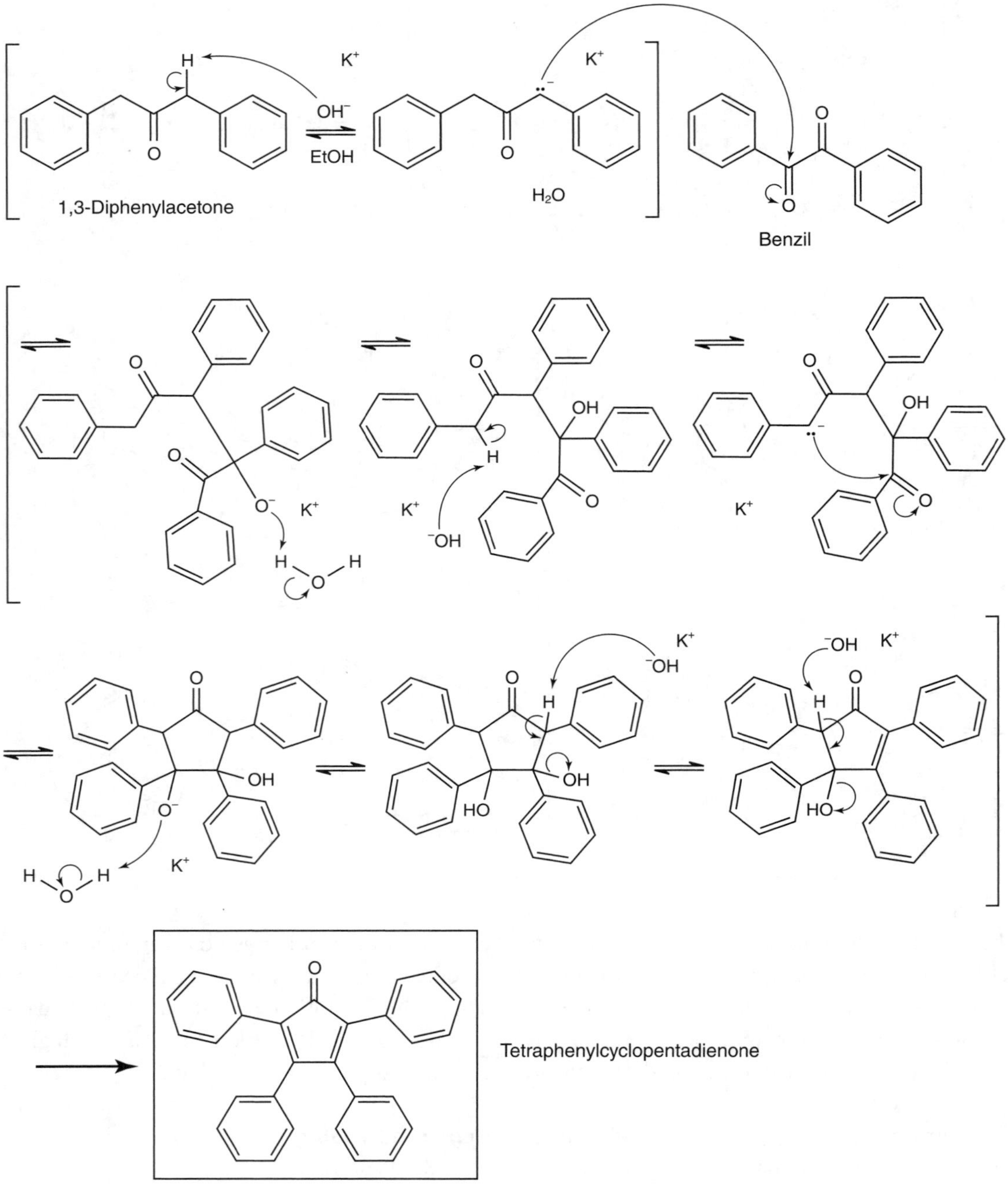

K⁺
OH⁻
EtOH
K⁺
H₂O
1,3-Diphenylacetone
Benzil
K⁺
⁻OH
K⁺
K⁺
H₂O
Tetraphenylcyclopentadienone

Aim of the Experiment
- Perform a multistep synthesis.

Learning Objectives
- Perform three synthesis steps in sequence.

- Learn reaction mechanisms of the three reactions.

- Write a formal lab report.

Safety Considerations
Concentrated nitric acid is highly corrosive. Wear gloves. It will burn your skin almost immediately, and any contaminated area should be washed with water for 15 minutes. The nitrogen oxide fumes are highly toxic and may cause inflammation of the lungs.

Ethanol KOH solution is corrosive, and any contaminated skin area should be thoroughly washed with water. Wear gloves.

Procedure
Benzoin Condensation of Benzaldehyde
This reaction should have been started in the previous lab period.

Tare the round-bottom flask and add about 1.5 mL of benzaldehyde and a magnetic stirrer. Determine the exact weight of the benzaldehyde used. In a vial, dissolve 225 mg of thiamine catalyst (~ 5% compared to benzaldehyde) in 0.67 mL water and 2.0 mL 95 % ethanol. Add this solution to the benzaldehyde. 3M NaOH is added dropwise while stirring until the solution is bright yellow. If the benzaldehyde separates from the solution as an oil, add more ethanol dropwise until a homogeneous solution is obtained.[4] Stopper the flask and place securely in your locker for at least 24 hours.

Work-up
The reaction product should crystallize out. Cool in ice-water bath to achieve complete crystallization just before filtration. Filter the product using the Hirsh funnel and wash the crystals three times with 2 mL of ice-cold 50 % ethanol / water to remove unreacted benzaldehyde. Leave the colorless or pale yellow crystals on the Hirsh funnel until dry. Weigh the crude material. Recrystallize from 95 % ethanol and isolate. Determine the weight of benzoin, the melting point, and record an IR spectrum.

Oxidation of Benzoin to Benzil
Place the benzoin from the previous reaction in a reaction flask along with a magnetic stirrer. Add 1 mL of concentrated nitric acid and place an air condenser on the flask and heat to 100 °C using a hot water bath. Remove the toxic nitrogen oxide gases as they form.[5] From the time the nitrogen oxide fumes start to form, heat for at least 30 minutes, until no more fumes are observed.

Work-up
Cool the reaction mixture for a few minutes, and then transfer the reaction mixture with a Pasteur pipet to a beaker containing 3 mL of water. Rinse the reaction flask with an additional mL of water and add to the beaker. Stir the aqueous mixture vigorously with a glass rod until the mixture has reached room temperature. The oily benzil should crystallize as a yellow solid.[6] Crush the solid with the glass rod and filter. Wash well with cold water to remove nitric acid. Leave the crystals on the funnel until dry.[7]

Weigh the crude benzil and recrystallize using 95 % ethanol. Seed the solution.[8] Yellow needle-like crystals are formed. Cool in ice water to achieve complete crystallization. Filter and air dry on the funnel. Weigh the product. Determine the melting point (lit.[9] 95 °C) and record the IR spectrum.

Synthesis of Tetraphenylcyclopentadienone
Preheat water bath to 80–100 °C.

Use all the benzil you synthesized in the previous step, but not more than 0.1 g. Add an equimolar amount of 1,3-diphenylacetone and mix with 1 mL of absolute ethanol in a reaction flask equipped with a magnetic stirrer and a water-cooled condenser. Heat with stirring until all the solids dissolve and the ethanol has reached reflux temperature. Using a Pasteur pipet, add slowly 0.15 mL of a 30 % ethanolic KOH solution through the top of the condenser.[10] Increase the temperature of the sand bath if necessary until a gentle reflux is observed and continue heating for 10–15 minutes.

Work-up
Cool the reaction mixture to room temperature and then in an ice-water bath for five minutes to complete crystallization. Filter the crystals using a Hirsh funnel. Wash the product three times with 0.5 mL of cold absolute ethanol and remove the magnetic stirrer. Leave the crystals in the Hirsh funnel until dry. Weigh the product, determine the melting point (lit. 218–220 °C) and, if possible,[11] record an IR spectrum. Show your product to your TA before disposing of it.

Optional recrystallization if melting point indicates the product is not pure enough: use a 1:1 mixture of absolute ethanol and toluene.

Notes
1. In strongly alkaline conditions benzaldehyde, like all other aldehydes without α-hydrogens, undergoes the Cannizzaro reaction, yielding benzyl alcohol and sodium benzoate.

2. Thiazoline is a five-membered ring with both a sulfur and a nitrogen atom. The thiazolium ion is the anion derived from thiazoline.

3. Again, benzil has no α-hydrogens and cannot form an enolate. Mixed aldol condensations between two reagents, of which only one can form an enolate, proceed in higher yield, as fewer side reactions are possible. Notice though that 1,3-diphenylacetone could undergo aldol condensation with itself, leading to side products.

4. If the solution darkens, i.e., goes from bright yellow to amber and dark amber, adding base will NOT restore the yellow color. In this case, add another ~200 mg of thiamine.

5. Use an inverted Büchner funnel connected to a vacuum as a mini-hood, or connect a Pasteur pipet to the house vacuum and insert it in the top of the condenser under slight vacuum.

6. Sometimes it is necessary to add seed crystals to achieve crystallization of the product.

7. This will probably take about 5 minutes.

8. This benzil solution in ethanol has a great tendency to become oversaturated and in most cases some form of seeding will be necessary, otherwise the crystals tend to just crash out. If the latter occurs, many impurities will be trapped in the crystals.

The solution can be seeded in two ways. If you dip a spatula in the solution, then you take it out to evaporate the solvent and dip it back in the solution to seed. The other method involves adding a little chunk of ice to the solution while the flask is being cooled in an ice bath. This both dilutes the solvent and also offers a sharp, cold object for the crystallization to start. Or you can scratch the side of the beaker with a spatula.

9. A benzil melting point as low as 84 °C is acceptable for the next step.

10. The reaction mixture will start to turn purple. If the reaction does not turn purple, add more base. Sometimes it does get stuck to the sides of the flask.

11. Tetraphenylcyclopentadienone is highly crystalline, and this makes it more difficult to record a spectrum using the IR cards. Try using dichloromethane. Students usually obtain pure product in this reaction, and the melting point should give a good indication of purity.

Discussion

• Explain the reaction conditions for each of the reactions.

• Explain the work-up procedures for each of these reactions.

• Comment on the effectiveness of these reactions.

• Comment on the purity and identification of each of your intermediate products.

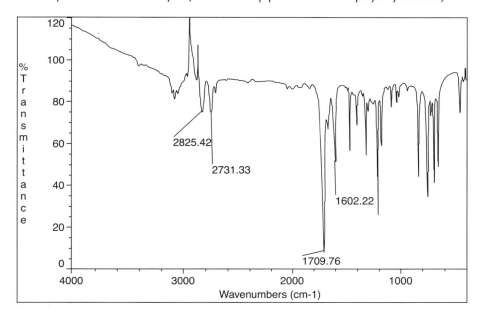

IR spectrum of benzaldehyde (note the sharp peaks due to the polyethylene film)

Questions

1. In the recrystallization of benzil, why do you have to cool the ethanol solution of benzil slowly?

2. In the third reaction, benzil was reacted with 1,3-diphenylacetone via a classical aldol reaction. What would happen if your reaction became wet? Show mechanism.

3. Draw the structure of the product you would expect from the reaction of benzaldehyde and acetophenone with base. Suggest several possible by-products of this reaction.

4. Given the following information, calculate the percent yield. 43 g A (MW 68), 36.6 g B (MW 76), and 30.8 g D (MW 85) were combined in a flask with an appropriate solvent. 20.5 g of E (MW 60) were isolated from the reaction. Indicate the limiting reagent and show all calculations.
   $2A + B \rightarrow 3C$
   $C + 2D \rightarrow 2E$

5. Why is water the first solvent introduced into the vial containing the thiamine hydrochloride?

10b

OFF, An Insect Repellent

Insect repellents are widely used in our society today. The compound you will be synthesizing is the most commonly used insect repellent, namely N,N–diethyl m–toluamide, also named OFF or Deet. It is effective against a wide variety of insects such as mosquitoes, fleas, and ticks. Exactly why some substances act as insect repellents has not been completely established, but extensive studies have been conducted on the effect of OFF on the mosquito. Mosquitoes have antennae that contain sensors for both carbon dioxide and water vapor. The carbon dioxide sensor is only temporarily disabled by OFF, but the sensor used for water vapor detection seems to be completely turned off by the insect repellent. Therefore the mosquito is not able to find its victim and it becomes completely confused.

In this experiment the starting material is the carboxylic acid, m–toluic acid. OFF is the corresponding amide of diethylamine. The most direct synthesis route to an amide would seem to be reaction of a carboxylic acid with an amine; however, in this case we are reacting an acid with a base, and a salt is formed, namely the ammonium salt. This salt can be converted to the carboxylic amide when this is salt is heated to very high temperatures, but this is obviously not a convenient laboratory synthesis.

$$R{-}COOH \ + \ R_2NH \ \longrightarrow \ RCOO^- \ R_2NH_2^+ \ \xrightarrow{\text{heat}} \ RCONR_2 \ + \ H_2O$$

Safety Considerations

If you have a known allergy to OFF (Deet), talk to your TA.

Thionyl chloride is very noxious and corrosive and should be handled with great care. Any contamination on the skin should be washed off immediately with lots of water or serious burns will result. **Thionyl chloride reacts violently with water, therefore dry glassware should be used when handling this chemical.** Do not breathe the fumes! Wear gloves.

Diethylamine is also noxious and corrosive. It has a low boiling point, 56 °C, and should be kept cool.

It is obvious that thionyl chloride and diethylamine should be stored separately, ideally in separate hoods.

HCl and SO_2 will be formed in this reaction, but the amounts are so small that it shouldn't bother anybody. The down-draft ventilation on the lab benches should take care of the fumes, or use a "mini-hood."

On a laboratory scale amides are usually prepared from the more reactive acid chloride. The carboxylic acid is converted to its acid chloride by reaction with an excess thionyl chloride, and the acid chloride is then reacted with the appropriate amine to form the amide. Excess base is used in these reactions to react with the hydrogen chloride formed.

Required Reading

- Acyl chlorides and Amides in your Organic Chemistry textbook

Aim of the Experiment

- Synthesize an amide using the acid chloride route.

Learning Objectives

- Learn about the usefulness of an acid chloride.

- Perform the reaction of an acid chloride with an amine.

- Perform an elaborate extraction procedure.

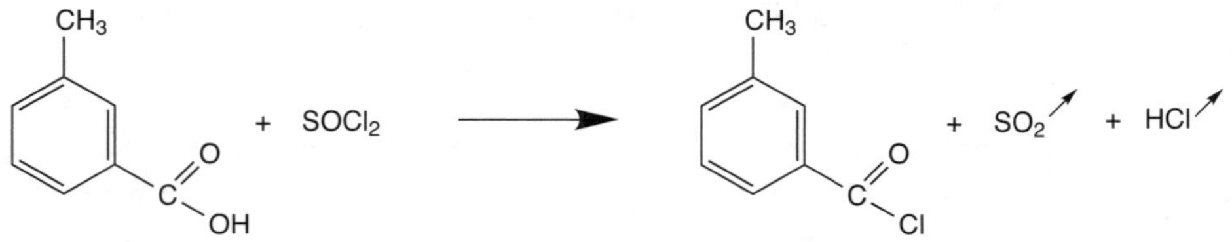

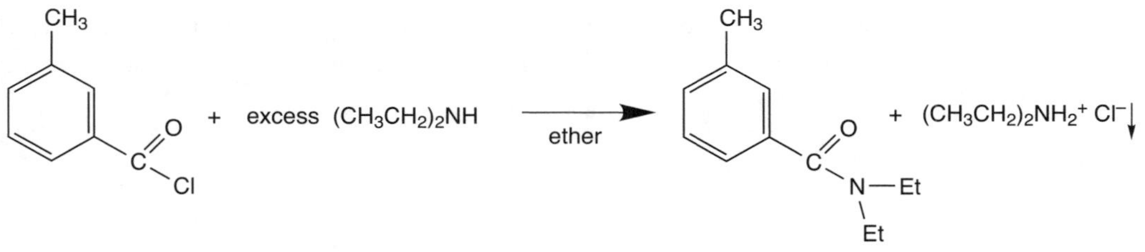

Procedure

Use a **dry** 10 mL round-bottom flask with a magnetic stirrer. Place the Claisen head on the flask. Cap the straight arm of the Claisen head with a septum and the other arm with a water condenser.

Place about 0.4 g of *m*-toluic acid in the reaction flask. Add a twofold excess of thionyl chloride[1], calculate the amount of thionyl chloride necessary (MW 119, d = 1.64 g/mL). Assemble the reaction apparatus. Heat to about 90 °C in a water bath or heating mantle for 15 minutes. Cool to room temperature. Turn off the hot plate if used.[2]

Add 4 mL of anhydrous ether using the syringe (through the septum) and stir until homogeneous. In the hood, mix diethylamine (MW 73, d = 0.71 g/mL), a threefold excess compared to *m*-toluic acid, with 1.5 mL of anhydrous ether. Add this mixture of diethylamine and ether **dropwise** to the reaction mixture using the syringe and continue stirring. The addition should take about 10–15 minutes. Diethylamine hydrochloride will precipitate from the reaction mixture. Stir for additional 10 minutes.

Work-up

Add 2 mL of a 5 % aqueous sodium hydroxide solution using the syringe. Stir for 15 minutes.[3] Two layers will form.[4] Transfer the reaction mixture to a test tube if it is difficult to see the two layers in the round-bottom flask. Remove the lower aqueous layer[5] and add another 2 mL of the 5 % NaOH aqueous solution, cap the vial or test tube and shake occasionally during 5 minutes. Allow the layers to separate and remove the lower aqueous layer.[6]

Extract the ether layer with 2 mL of a 10 % HCl aqueous solution.[7] Finally, wash the ether layer with 2 mL of water. For each extraction, shake the mixture, allow the two layers to separate and remove the aqueous layer; add ether as necessary.

Transfer the ether layer with a dry pipet to a vial and add granular anhydrous sodium sulfate.[8] When dry, transfer the ether solution to a small beaker. Wash the drying agent with a little additional ether to ensure all product has been transferred. Evaporate the ether on a moderately warm hot plate.[9] The residue will be dark brown; this is the crude amide.

Prepare a small alumina column in a Pasteur pipet to purify this product. A column of about 2 cm in height should be sufficient and use the Dry Pack Method to pack the column. Dissolve the crude product in a minimal amount of hexane. Use hexane to moisten the column, and when the eluent level has reached the top of the packing material, add the solution of the crude product to the top of the column. Use hexane as the eluent, once all the product has been absorbed on the column. Collect the eluting solvent containing the product in a preweighed beaker; it should be a yellow solution. Evaporate the hexane on a warm hot plate, using an air stream to speed up evaporation. *N,N*–Diethyl *m*–toluamide should be a light tan liquid.

Determine the yield. Record an IR spectrum.

Notes

1. Excess thionyl chloride is used, as some will be lost during the reaction time because it is so volatile and to speed up the reaction.

2. The next reaction step is performed at room temperature. You might have to use an insulating pad to avoid heating the ether mixture used in the next step.

3. Sodium hydroxide will react with any remaining acid chloride to form the sodium salt of the carboxylic acid, which is soluble in the aqueous layer during the extraction. Diethylamine hydrochloride is also water soluble. Any remaining thionyl chloride will be destroyed by the water, resulting in SO_2 and HCl. The latter is of course neutralized by NaOH.

4. The desired product, N,N–diethyl toluamide is soluble in ether.

5. As in any extraction, you should NEVER discard any of the solutions until you are sure the product is recovered. Never be too sure that your product is where you think it is.

6. Add additional ether if too much solvent is lost due to evaporation during these extractions.

7. Any remaining diethylamine will react with HCl to form the hydrochloride salt, making it water soluble.

8. Sodium sulfate is a drying agent used in acidic conditions. Use enough sodium sulfate so that the ether solution will turn clear. About two spatula tips should be sufficient.

9. Create an air stream over the solution by connecting a hose to the vacuum on the bench. This will increase the evaporation rate, while also reducing the ether vapors in the lab.

Discussion

• Discuss the logic of the synthetic scheme.

• Discuss the extraction procedure in detail; i.e., which components are extracted at each stage?

• Discuss the identification of your product.

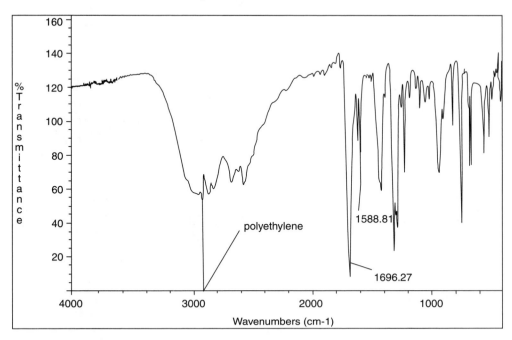

IR Spectrum of m–*Toluic Acid*

IR spectrum of relatively pure OFF (N,N–diethyl m–toluamide)

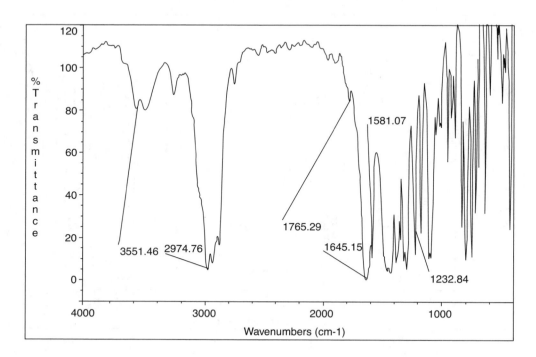

IR spectrum of impure OFF

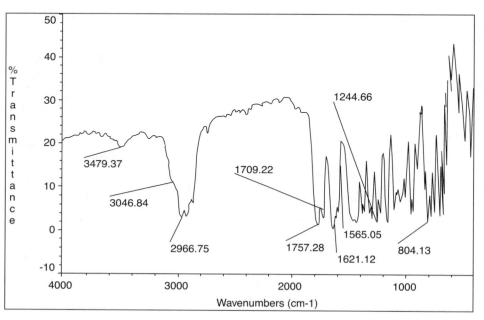

Questions

1. Why do you wash the reaction mixture of *N,N*–diethyl–*m*–toluamide with two portions of NaOH solution?

2. A student performed today's reaction, but decided he or she was in a hurry and wanted to leave lab. Therefore no extractions were done, saving a half hour. You ran an IR and NMR on his/her final product to determine the purity of the compound. The spectrum is shown on the previous page on the bottom. Label all peaks that are significant, including impurities if present in the IR.

3. How would you remove the above impurities that you labeled. (Assume your TA is stupid! Give details: solvents, chemicals, procedure (i.e., filtration), as well as the reaction).

4. Write down the reaction that would happen if you took the product from step one and added water to the reaction.

5. Why can't we make the amide directly from the acid and the amine?

6. Write out a stepwise mechanism for the second reaction performed in this lab.

7. Adipic acid (HOOC–$CH_2CH_2CH_2CH_2$–COOH, 15 g) is treated with excess thionyl chloride, and the resulting acid dichloride is reacted with 20 mL butyl amine (d = 0.74). After work-up and recrystallization, 12.5 g of *N,N'*–dibutyl adipamide is obtained. What is the limiting reagent? Calculate the % yield.

Synthesis of a Dye, Methyl Orange

People have been using dyes since the beginning of time for different purposes, such as drawing pictures, dying hair, applying face colors, and dying fabrics. Natural dyes include madder (a brilliant red dye derived from a root), indigo, and several variations of brown, yellow, and green. But plant dyes do not offer the great variety and brilliance offered by the synthetic dyes. Today we have available an infinite spectrum of colors to dye any type of fabric.

mauve

Many of the early synthetic dyes were derived from aniline ($PhNH_2$) or related aromatic amines. In the mid 1850s an English chemist, W.H. Perkin, was trying to synthesize quinine by oxidizing allyltoluidine with potassium dichromate. He tried this because the molecular formula

FD&C Yellow #3

FD&C Yellow #6

FD&C Red #32

FD&C Orange #4

FD&C Orange #1

Methyl Orange

Butter Yellow

of quinine is exactly twice the molecular formula of allyltoluidine. This turned out to be an erroneous idea and no quinine was obtained. However he did see a reddish-brown precipitate which turned out to be a good dye for fabrics. When he used aniline, he obtained a black precipitate, which upon extraction with ethanol yielded a beautiful purple color. The purple solution also turned out to be very efficient at dying fabric and became known as *mauve*. It has a rather complicated structure as shown, and also shows that Perkin's aniline was contaminated with toluidines (amine-substituted toluenes). As a side comment, the black precipitate Perkin obtained was "Aniline Black." Aniline Black is the polymer of aniline, a conducting organic polymer which has been thoroughly investigated during the last twenty years. It has been shown that polyaniline can be processed into conducting fibers and films with numerous technological applications.

About ten years after the first synthesis of mauve, the azo dyes were discovered by Griess. These azo dyes revolutionized the dye industry and they are still the most common dyes, from food dyes, fabric dyes, and printing inks to pigments in paint. They all have the same basic structure, namely Ar–N=N–Ar, in which Ar represents any aromatic group. The –N=N– functionality is called an azo group. The extended conjugated system is a strong chromophore, giving these compounds their brilliant colors. The specific color depends on the nature of the aromatic group and the substituents. Many of these colors are FD&C colors (food, drug, and cosmetics) and are safe, while others are carcinogenic. All the azo dyes are synthesized using the same basic reaction, namely an azo coupling between a diazonium ion and an aromatic substrate.

Required Reading
- Azo coupling in your Organic Chemistry textbook.

Aim of the Experiment
- Synthesize the synthetic dye.

- Test the coloring qualities of the dye.

- Test the dye as a pH indicator.

- Bleach the dye.

Learning Objectives
- Learn about the synthesis of azo dyes.

- Observe the interactions of the dye with different fabrics.

- Learn about bleaching.

Reaction Mechanism
Azo coupling occurs between a diazonium salt and an activated aromatic substrate. The mechanism is an electrophilic aromatic substitution in which the positively charged diazonium ion

is the electrophile. Therefore the same rules as for any electrophilic aromatic substitution apply: electron-donating groups such as amines, ethers and alkyl groups activate the aromatic substrate and are ortho-para directors, while groups such as carboxylic esters and nitro groups are deactivators and meta directors.

The first step in an azo coupling is the formation of the diazonium ion intermediate, which is formed by reaction of an aromatic amine with nitrous acid. This process is called *diazotation*. Nitrous acid is formed *in situ* by reaction of sodium nitrite and hydrochloric acid. For the reaction in this experiment, the diazonium ion of sulfanilic acid has to be formed. However, sulfanilic acid is not soluble in acidic solution, and the medium in this reaction has to be acidic to form the nitrous acid. This problem is circumvented by dissolving the sulfanilic acid first in alkaline solution by addition of sodium carbonate. At the beginning of the reaction, when HCl is added, two things will happen: nitrous acid will be formed *in situ* and the sulfanilic acid will precipitate out as a very finely divided precipitate, which is highly reactive. The diazonium salt of the sulfanilic acid will be formed, which is also insoluble in the reaction medium, but again very finely divided. The diazonium ion will react immediately with the highly reactive *N,N*–dimethylaniline to form methyl orange.

Methyl orange is an acid base indicator: At pH > 4.4, methyl orange exists mostly as the yellow negative sulfonate ion, while at pH < 3.2 the dipolar red ion (helianthin) predominates. In higher concentration in basic solution, methyl orange does appear as orange.

It is rather easy to bleach azo dyes. Reducing agents such as sodium hydrosulfite, $Na_2S_2O_4$,

or stannous chloride in HCl, are often used. They reduce the azo bond to the two amine functionalities.

Procedure

Diazonium Salt Formation

In a small Erlenmeyer flask, dissolve 0.06 g of sodium carbonate in about 5 mL of water. Add 0.2 g of sulfanilic acid monohydrate and heat to reflux until it is homogeneous. Cool to room temperature and add 0.08 g of sodium nitrite and stir until homogeneous. Cool in an ice water bath for 5–10 minutes until the temperature is below 10 °C. Add 0.25 mL concentrated hydrogen chloride to the solution. The diazonium salt should precipitate as a finely divided white precipitate. Keep this solution cold.

Azo Coupling

In a vial or flask, mix 0.14 mL of *N,N*–dimethyl-aniline with 0.10 mL of glacial acetic acid. Add this solution dropwise to the diazonium salt suspension. Stir vigorously with a spatula.[1] Keep cold. A red precipitate will start to form. Cool the reaction mixture for another ten minutes in the ice bath. **Slowly** add 1.5 mL of a 10 % NaOH aqueous solution. Check the pH of the

$$Ar—N{=}N—Ar' \xrightarrow{Na_2S_2O_4} Ar—NH_2 \; + \; Ar'—NH_2$$

reaction mixture with pH paper to ensure that the solution is basic. If not, add more NaOH.

Work-up

Reflux for 10–15 minutes. Most methyl orange will dissolve. Add ~0.5 g of NaCl[2] and allow the mixture to cool first to room temperature and then in the ice bath. Filter and rinse the reaction flask twice with saturated aqueous NaCl solution and wash the filter cake with these rinse solutions.

Transfer the product into about 15 mL of boiling water in a beaker and continue heating for a few minutes while stirring with a glass rod. Most of the dye will dissolve, but not all, but all the contaminating salts will dissolve. Cool in the ice bath and filter using a Büchner funnel. Dry the product on the Büchner funnel by maintaining the vacuum for 5–10 minutes. Determine the yield.

Dyeing Test

Obtain a strip of Multifiber Fabric from your TA. The identity of the different fabrics will be posted in the lab, and they range from nylon and polyester to cotton and silk.[3] The dye mixture consists of ~50 mg of methyl orange in 30 mL of water containing 1 mL of 15 % aqueous sodium sulfate solution and 1 drop of concentrated sulfuric acid. Heat to just below boiling and immerse the fabric strip in the dye bath for ~10 minutes. Rinse the fabric well with lots of water. Note the different dye colors on the different fabrics.

Bleaching

You can either bleach the dye bath itself, or the dyed fabric strip.

To bleach the dye bath, add sodium carbonate until basic. Then add a solution of sodium hydrosulfite ($Na_2S_2O_4$, sodium dithionite) until the dye color disappears. Add a slight excess of sodium hydrosulfite.

To bleach the fabric, add the fabric strip to this bleached dye bath or to a basic solution of sodium hydrosulfite in water.

Methyl Orange As an Indicator

In a test tube, dissolve a few methyl orange crystals in a small amount of water. Watch the color switch from orange to red as you alternately add acid (dilute HCl) and base (dilute NaOH).

Note

1. A plastic spatula works fine.

2. Addition of NaCl is a common practice in organic synthesis known as "salting out." The solubility of the organic compound in aqueous medium is reduced by the addition of salt, thereby facilitating the separation of organic and aqueous parts. The same principle is often used to aid in the separation of organic and aqueous layers in liquid–liquid extractions.

3. Clip one end of the fabric strip so that you can still identify the different fabrics once they are dyed.

Discussion

• Discuss the azo dye synthesis procedure.

• Comment on the versatility of the azo dyes.

• Discuss the interactions of the dye with the different fabrics.

• Discuss bleaching.

• Discuss the behavior of these dyes at varying pH.

Questions

1. How do you break a diazo linkage?

2. Why does the addition of acid to methyl orange cause a color change? Hint: compare the conjugation lengths.

3. What would be the result if cuprous chloride were added to the diazonium salt prepared in this reaction?

4. Methyl orange was synthesized using a diazo-coupling reaction. Show how you would synthesize Yellow #3 and Red #32 dyes using the diazo coupling reaction.

5. Draw the resonance structures for the methyl orange in acidic solution.

12b

Polymers

Polymers are usually chainlike molecules of extremely high molecular weight. Polymers can also be three-dimensional, and in this case networks are formed. Polymers are synthesized by normal organic reactions, with the caveat that these reactions have to be highly efficient and have to proceed in > 99 % yield. Otherwise the molecular weights necessary to achieve good physical properties will not be achieved. The excellent physical properties of polymers can manifest themselves in fiber strength, elasticity, film properties, fire resistance, scratch resistance, optical clarity, etc. These properties all have their origin in the chemical structure of the polymer. Improvements to the physical properties of polymers can be made by either changing the chemical structure of the polymer or by processing. Processing of polymers is the realm of the engineers, while the modification of chemical structure still leads chemists to the discovery of new polymeric structures with novel properties.

A rather new field in polymer science is the synthesis of high-tech polymers. These polymers have certain high-tech applications in addition to their excellent physical properties. This has led researchers to the discovery of conducting polymers, of piezoelectric polymers (pressure on a piezoelectric material is transformed into an electric signal and vice versa), optical fibers for modern communication, nonlinear optical polymers with applications in optical computing and laser technology, etc. It is clear that the application of polymers in our modern society has

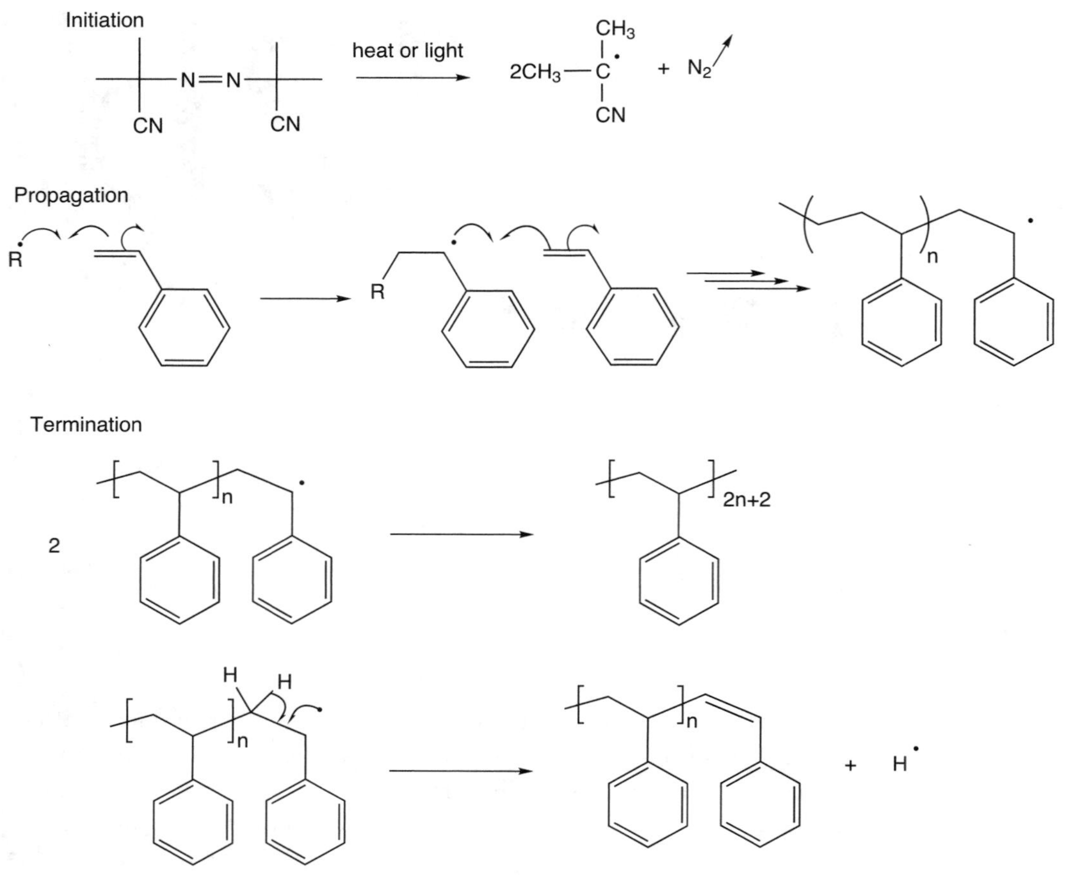

Initiation

Propagation

Termination

far from reached its limits, and the discovery of new polymers and polymer processes continues every day.

There are two basic categories of polymers based on the reaction mechanism by which they are synthesized, namely addition or chain polymers, and condensation polymers.

As the name implies, *addition* polymers are made by continuous addition of monomer units to a growing center. These polymerizations proceed via a chain reaction, meaning once a growing center is formed, the monomers add very fast until the chain is terminated. The growing center can be either free radical, cationic or anionic. The monomers are vinyl monomers,

meaning they contain a double bond. Cyclic monomers can also polymerize via a chain mechanism. A simple example of an addition polymer is polystyrene. The free radical polymerization of styrene has been well documented.[1] In the initiation step, a free radical initiator, such as AIBN (2,2′–azo–bisisobutyronitrile) decomposes to form free radicals. These free radicals can then react with a styrene molecule, resulting in a new bond and a new free radical, which in turn reacts with another styrene molecule, and so on. This is called the propagation step. In an ideal situation the growing chain would never die, and this is called living polymerization. However with most polymerization mechanisms, termination mechanisms exist which result in the loss of the growing center.

In the case of the free radical polymerization of styrene, termination can occur by recombination of two radical chains or by elimination of a β–hydrogen, which can in turn start another polymerizing chain.[2]

Polycondensation is a stepwise mechanism of polymerization. Bifunctional molecules react with each other to first form dimers, then tetramers, and higher molecular weight products. The molecular weight increases as the reaction progresses. Examples of polymers synthesized via a polycondensation reaction include polyesters, polyamides, polyimides, and polyurethanes. In a polyester, the ester functionalities are formed during the polymerization step. As an example the synthesis of Dacron is shown, which is formed by reaction of terephthalic acid and ethylene glycol (1,2–dihydroxyethane). Water is formed as a side product in this reaction.

Aim of the Experiment
- Explore the world of polymers.

Learning Objectives
- Learn about free radical chain polymerization.

- Explore condensation polymerizations wih di- and tri-substituted ingredients.

- Learn more about interfacial polymerization.

- Make a foam polyurethane.

Safety Considerations
Toluene diisocyanate (TDI), styrene, and methyl methacrylate are toxic. They will irritate the skin and eyes. Avoid breathing the vapors.

Azo-bis-isobutyronitrile (AIBN) is toxic and can decompose explosively when a large amount is heated.

Adipic acid is an irritant.

Methanol is flammable and toxic. It can cause blindness and death if ingested.

Background and Procedures

General Instructions
Very little glassware should be used in this lab; use mostly weighing boats and paper cups. Polymers can be rather difficult to dissolve, therefore we use disposable containers.

The brown paper on top of the benches is to make the cleanup easier for the preproom. Place wax paper on top of the brown paper, to make your cleanup easier.

Free Radical Copolymerization of Methyl Methacrylate and Styrene
Polystyrene is a very common polymer. More than 8 billion pounds of styrene (St) is polymerized annually in the US. Styrofoam cups, food containers, tape and CD cases are made from polystyrene. Polystyrene, however, is

terephthalic acid   ethylene glycol

somewhat brittle. Methyl methacrylate (MMA), $CH_2=C(CH_3)COOCH_3$, is also a frequently used monomer. One form of the polymer is commercially known as Plexiglass. However it is twice as expensive as polystyrene. A *copolymer* of the two monomers has better properties than either homopolymer, it lacks the brittleness of polystyrene and is cheaper than the poly(methyl methacrylate).

Mechanistically, this copolymer is formed in the same way as the polystyrene homopolymer described above, namely by attack of a growing free radical on either monomer. Here again, a free radical initiator is needed to *initiate* the polymerization. The radical adds to either a St monomer unit or an MMA molecule, regenerating the radical center in this *propagation* step. The monomer units can be incorporated in the polymer chain at different rates, depending on the monomer reactivity and the concentration, etc., resulting in different types of copolymers. If we designate St as monomer #1 M_1 and MMA as M_2, and both monomers are present in almost equal concentrations and have almost equal reactivity, a random copolymer will be obtained, which would look something like this:

random copolymer
$\sim M_1M_2M_1M_1M_2M_2M_1M_2M_2M_1M_2M_2\sim$

If one monomer is much more reactive than the other one, or if a growing free radical polymer end group of one monomer prefers to react with its own parent, rather than with the other monomer, blocks can be formed, resulting in the following structure

block copolymer
$\sim M_1M_1M_1M_1M_1M_1M_2M_2M_2M_2M_1M_1M_1\sim$

On the other hand, the growing free radical might prefer to react with the other monomer rather than with its own parent, and this would lead to alternating copolymers

alternating copolymer
$\sim M_1M_2M_1M_2M_1M_2M_1M_2\sim$

The behavior of two monomers in a copolymerization can be presented in a copolymerization curve, such as the one shown here for the free radical copolymerization of styrene and methyl methacrylate. In this graph, the x-axis represents the monomer feed composition, f_1, namely the mole fraction of styrene in the comonomer feed. In this graph, the 0 point represents a monomer feed containing no St, only pure MMA; therefore the mole fraction of St is zero. At the 0.5 point, we have equal molar concentrations of St and MMA, and at the 1.0 point, pure St, no MMA.

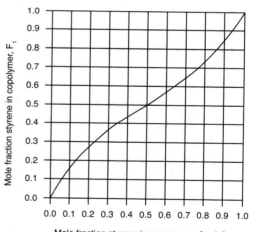

Mole fraction styrene in comonomer feed, f_1

The monomer feed is subjected to polymerization conditions, i.e., a free radical initiator is added and the mixture is heated to initiate the polymerization. After a certain time, the polymerization is stopped, and the copolymer is examined. How much St and MMA is present in the copolymer? In our experiment, we will use IR to determine this. The curve represents the result of this experiment, based on the data of many researchers. The y-axis represents the molar concentration of styrene in the copolymer, F_1. So what does this graph tell us? If we use a monomer feed with an f_1 value of 0.3 (30 mol% of the monomer feed is styrene, the remaining 70 mol % is MMA), we obtain a copolymer with an F_1 value of 0.38, so a copolymer containing ~38 mol % St and ~62 mol% MMA. On the other hand, a comonomer feed with an f_1 value of 0.8 will lead to copolymer with a F_1 value of 0.73, i.e. ~73 mol % St and ~27 mol% MMA.

In this experiment, your lab class will test their laboratory skills. Each of you will run a copolymerization of St and MMA at a different feed ratio, and the results will be collected on a copolymerization graph. How close does your class match the literature results?

Procedure

The TA will assign each student in the class a comonomer feed composition. Determine the amount of St and MMA necessary, so that the total weight of the monomers is between 350 and 450 mg. Assemble a 5 mL round-bottom flask or conical vial with a stir bar and a water condenser. Add 10 mg AIBN (2,2′–azabisisobutyronitrile) and then add the monomers, using a syringe. Lower the reaction flask into a water bath at 80 °C and heat for 15 minutes. Add two drops of methanol to stop the reaction, and cool the reaction vessel.

Add about 3 mL of chloroform to dissolve the polymer. Make sure any gel which might have formed in the bottom of the vial is dissolved. Add the chloroform solution dropwise to 50 mL of vigorously stirred methanol in a 100 mL or 250 mL beaker. (Check a big stir bar from the preproom.) A white precipitate will form. Filter the solution and dry the precipitated polymer for 5 minutes on top of the filter. Weigh the polymer. Record the IR spectrum. Label the carbonyl stretch at 1725 cm⁻¹ and the aromatic out-of-plane stretch (oops) at 698 cm⁻¹. Print two copies of the IR spectrum.

Determine the ratio of the oops/C=O peaks by measuring the area of the peaks by the peak height times width at half height method. The percent styrene in the copolymer can be determined by plugging the oops/C=O ratio in the equation

$$y = 0.644 x + 0.283$$

in which x is the oops/C=O ratio and y is the mol % styrene in the polymer.

Each lab section will have a theoretical copolymer composition curve on the bulletin board. Plot your data on the graph and judge for yourself how accurate the results of your class are.

For people interested in more details about the copolymerization, and the math behind this graph, read the footnote.[3]

Polyesterification

Two different polyesterification will be performed; one will result in a linear polyester and the other one in a cross-linked polyester. Phthalic anhydride is reacted with either ethylene glycol (1,2–dihydroxyethane) or glycerol (1,2,3–trihydroxypropane). Phthalic anhydride is used so the ester bonds can be formed without formation of water. The reaction of a diacid with a diol is shown in the Introduction and in that case one molecule of water is formed for each ester bond formed.

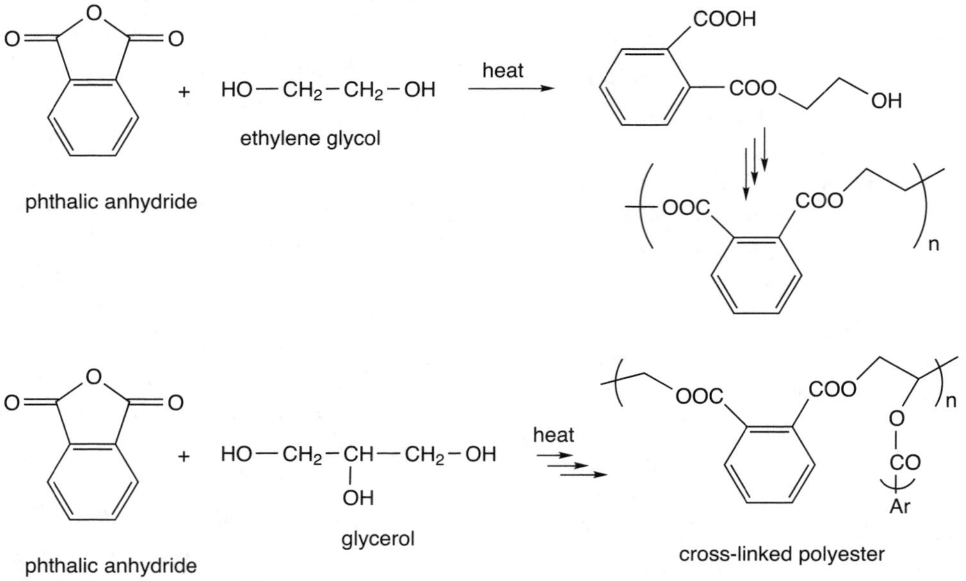

The reaction of phthalic anhydride and ethylene glycol leads to an isomeric polyester of Dacron. If more functional groups are present in the alcohol moiety, a cross-linked material will be obtained, as illustrated below for glycerol.

Procedure
Place 1 g of phthalic anhydride in each of two aluminum weighing boats, and add ~50 mg of sodium acetate (catalyst) to each. Add 0.4 mL ethylene glycol to the first aluminum pan, and 0.4 mL glycerol to the second one. Heat both on top of the hot plate. The mixture will appear to boil and heat for at least another 5 minutes. Cool the polymers and compare viscosity and brittleness of the two polymers.

Polyamide
Amide bonds are efficiently formed by reaction of an acid chloride and an amine, as was illustrated in the synthesis of OFF. For the synthesis of a polyamide, this same reaction is used, but now with difunctional monomers. For the synthesis of nylon, adipoyl chloride is reacted with 1,6–hexanediamine (hexamethylene-diamine) in the presence of a base to neutralize the hydrochloric acid formed in this reaction. It is obvious that a family of linear polyamides can be synthesized with a different number of carbons between the successive amide bonds, and this will be determined by the dicarboxylic acid and the diamine used. Commercial nylon is better defined as Nylon–6,6, in which the first 6 indicates the number of carbons in the dicarboxylic acid (adipic acid) and the second 6 the number of carbons in the diamine (hexamethylene diamine).

The polyamide formation will be run in a two-phase system. An aqueous layer will contain hexamethylenediamine and NaOH as base

adipoyl chloride   hexamethylenediamine

NaOH   −NaCl

Nylon–6,6

to neutralize the acid formed in the reaction. Adipoyl chloride will be dissolved in the hexane layer. Reaction will occur at the interface of the water and hexane layers, and is called an "interfacial polymerization." The reaction is very fast, and as soon as the hexane layer is poured on top of the water layer, a "skin" will form between the two layers. This is the nylon, which can be pulled out with a spatula.

Procedure

In a 50 or 100 mL beaker, place 10 mL of 15 % aqueous solution of hexamethylenediamine and add 1–2 drops of phenolphthalein. Carefully add 10 mL of a 5 % solution of adipoyl chloride in cyclohexane by pouring it down the wall of the slightly tilted beaker. Two layers will seen. Immediately a film will form between the two layers. Using a copper wire or a spatula, hook the film at the center and gently pull. The polyamide will form continuously, producing a rope that can be pulled out for many feet. The

cardboard roll inside a paper towel package works great. Rinse the rope with water and dry on top of a paper towel. The remainder of the solutions in the beaker can be mixed with the spatula or copper wire, and a big blob of nylon will form. Remove the polymer from the solution and wash with water. Dry the polymer.

The nylon strands are very, very long. Try to calculate how many monomer units it would take to obtain this length of fiber. You'll be amazed.

Polyurethane

Polyurethanes are used extensively as foams, for example, for mattresses and foam furniture parts. The foaming of the polymer occurs during the polymerization because CO_2 is formed as one of the side reactions. The amount of foaming can be controlled by the amount of water added to the polymerizing mixture.

toluene diisocyanate   glycerol   cross-linked polyurethane

A urethane functionality (–NH–CO–O–) is formed by reaction of an isocyanate functionality (–N=C=O) with an alcohol. The alcohol adds across the N=C double bond of the isocyanate.

A linear polyurethane would be formed upon addition of a diisocyanate to a diol, but most polyurethanes which are fabricated are cross-linked polymers. Glycerol, 1,2,3–trihydroxypropane, is used as the alcohol component and toluene diisocyanate as the isocyanate. In addition some water is added, which upon reaction with water forms a primary amine and CO_2. The carbon dioxide forms bubbles in the viscous polymerizing mass. Silicone oil and castor oil are also added to the mix, along with stannous octanoate as a catalyst. On an industrial scale, all reaction components except for the toluene diisocyanate are mixed together as mixture A. Mixture B mostly contains toluene diisocyanate.

Procedure

In a paper cup, pour 8.5 mL of mixture A and add 5 mL of mixture B (toluene diisocyanate). Stir the mixture rapidly with a glass rod until smooth and creamy. The reaction mixture should become warm and bubbles of carbon dioxide should start forming. Stop stirring. Do not breathe the vapors. Once foaming has subsided, allow the polymer to cool to room temperature. It will be sticky initially, but firm up after a while. The material will also shrink with time.

Notes

1. Styrene can also polymerize via a cationic or an anionic mechanism.

2. Loss of a β–hydrogen from a growing chain and reinitiation by this new free radical is called a transfer reaction.

3. The composition of the copolymer, whether random, block, or alternating, is dependent on the reactivity of the terminal unit or growth center (free radical in our case) towards each particular monomer. In a free radical copolymerization, two reactive species (a terminal styrene or MMA radical in our case) are possible at the growing center. As the chain propagates, M_1^* and M_2^* react with either monomer M_1 or monomer M_2. The four possible reactions and rate constants are shown below:

$$\sim\!\sim\!\sim M_1^* + M_1 \xrightarrow{\ k_{11}\ } \sim\!\sim\!\sim M_1M_1^*$$

$$\sim\!\sim\!\sim M_1^* + M_2 \xrightarrow{\ k_{12}\ } \sim\!\sim\!\sim M_1M_2^*$$

$$\sim\!\sim\!\sim M_2^* + M_1 \xrightarrow{\ k_{21}\ } \sim\!\sim\!\sim M_2M_1^*$$

$$\sim\!\sim\!\sim M_2^* + M_2 \xrightarrow{\ k_{22}\ } \sim\!\sim\!\sim M_2M_2^*$$

The rate constants k_{11} and k_{22} describe the reaction of M_1^* with its parent M_1 and the reaction of M_2^* with its parent M_2, respectively. These reactions are homopropagations, and these are the reactions that occur in either homopolymerization. In the copolymerization we also get cross-propagation reactions, described by the rate constants k_{12} and k_{21} from the reaction of M_1^* with the other monomer M_2 and of M_2^* with M_1, respectively. The monomer reactivity ratios r_1 and r_2 are defined as the ratio of the rate constant for homopropagation divided by the rate constant for cross-propagation.

$$r_1 = \frac{k_{11}}{k_{12}} \qquad r_{12} = \frac{k_{22}}{k_{21}}$$

An r value greater than 1 means the propagating species favors homopropagation, while a value of less than 1 means that cross-propagation is favored. A perfectly alternating copolymerization would have r values approaching zero.

The composition of the final polymer can be determined using the following equation in which f_1 and f_2 are the mole fractions of M_1 and M_2 in the comonomer feed, while F_1 and F_2 are the mole fractions in the polymer of each monomer, respectively:

$$F_1 = \frac{r_1f_1^2 + f_1f_2}{r_1f_1^2 + 2f_1f_2 + r_2f_2^2}$$

The r_1 and r_2 values for the free radical copolymerization of styrene and methyl methacrylate have been determined experimentally by several researchers, and have been found to be 0.52 and 0.46, respectively.

Questions

1. Vinylidene chloride, $CH_2=CCl_2$, is copolymerized with vinyl chloride to make Saran. Write a structure that includes at least two units for the copolymer that is formed.

2. Isobutylene, $CH_2=C(CH_3)_2$, is used to prepare cold-flow rubber. Write a structure for the addition polymer formed from this alkene.

3. Define an addition polymer and a condensation polymer. Give an example for each type.

4. Maleic anhydride reacts with ethylene glycol, $HOCH_2CH_2OH$, to produce an alkyl resin. Write the structure of the condensation polymer produced.